PUFFIN BOOKS

Editor: Kaye Webb

PS174

HUNT ROYAL

This is the true story of a man-hunt; an entire army in pursuit of a king. For six weeks Oliver Cromwell's army chased the brave and debonair Charles II through the west and south-west of England, in a series of adventures which outdo the most exciting tales of make-believe. But because over fifty people were willing to risk their lives and ignore the fortune in gold which would result from his capture, he managed to get away to France and safety, and nine years later returned in triumph to reward those who had saved him.

David Scott Daniell has given us a history lesson without tears; he has recreated every step of the king's dangerous flight with a wealth of careful detail, and there is a map of his zig-zag journey which makes the story even more vivid.

Everyone from nine years old will enjoy it

David Scott Daniell

HUNT ROYAL

WITH ILLUSTRATIONS BY
WILLIAM STOBBS

PENGUIN BOOKS

Penguin Books Ltd, Harmondsworth, Middlesex
AUSTRALIA: Penguin Books Pty Ltd, 762 Whitehorse Road,
Mitcham, Victoria

—

First published by Jonathan Cape 1958
Published in Puffin Books 1962

—

Copyright © David Scott Daniell, 1958

—

Made and printed in Great Britain
by Richard Clay & Company Ltd,
Bungay, Suffolk
Set in Monotype Plantin

CONTENTS

STAFFORD

Hobbal Grange Whiteladies House
Boscobel House
Madeley Moseley Hall
Bentley Hall

SHROP-
SHIRE
WARWICK-

WORCESTER-
SHIRE

Long Marston

GLOUCESTER-
SHIRE

N

WILT-
SHIRE

BRISTOL
CHANNEL

Abbots Leigh

HAMP-
SHIRE

Heale House

SOMERSET

Salisbury

Trent House

Broadwindsor

Broadhalfpenny
Down

Charmouth

DORSET

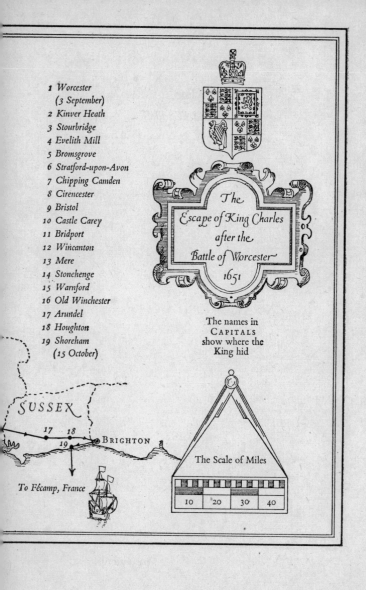

1 Worcester
  (3 September)
2 Kinver Heath
3 Stourbridge
4 Evelith Mill
5 Bromsgrove
6 Stratford-upon-Avon
7 Chipping Camden
8 Cirencester
9 Bristol
10 Castle Carey
11 Bridport
12 Wincanton
13 Mere
14 Stonehenge
15 Warnford
16 Old Winchester
17 Arundel
18 Houghton
19 Shoreham
  (15 October)

The Escape of King Charles after the Battle of Worcester 1651

The names in
CAPITALS
show where the
King hid

SUSSEX

17 18 BRIGHTON
  19

To Fécamp, France

The Scale of Miles

10 20 30 40

For
Bertha Waddell

CHAPTER ONE

WORCESTER FIGHT

THIS is the story of a man-hunt. A whole army and most of the country hunted one man – the King of England. He was alone, except for a handful of devoted friends, and capture would mean almost certain death. The hunters were the army of Oliver Cromwell, the quarry was King Charles II. The hunt lasted six weeks, through the west and south-west of England, a series of adventures which would be hard to believe in a story-book. Yet it really happened.

The story begins on a bright September morning three hundred years ago, on 3rd September 1651. The King, a handsome young man of twenty-one, stood on the top of the tower of Worcester cathedral. He wore richly chased armour, with the blue riband of the Order of the Garter across his breast, and the slight breeze stirred his long dark hair. A group of half a dozen men, also in armour, stood together at a respectful distance.

The King's title was only recognized in Scotland and Ireland, in England he was known as Charles Stuart, the rebel. When his father had been executed two years earlier, Parliament had ordained that its power was supreme and there should be no King of England. So the Army of the King, which was mainly Scottish, and the Army of Parliament, commanded by Oliver Cromwell, faced each other before the city of Worcester to decide the issue.

More than forty-five thousand men stood to arms in the green meadows round Worcester. The Royal Army held the city, and waited in Fort Royal just outside, and lined the hedges and lanes. The Army of Cromwell, twice as numerous as the King's, was waiting beyond the rivers Severn and Teme to launch their attack.

From the cathedral tower the young King could see the countryside spread below him like a map. He studied the positions, making sure that every regiment was posted where it could most effectively meet the enemy when he attacked. He looked down to see his cavalry waiting by their horses in the meadows against the city walls. Then he looked slowly along the fields leading down to the river, where his regiments of Foot were posted.

In one of the fields a Scottish boy sat on a tussock of grass, idly whittling a stick with his knife. He yawned with nervousness, tried to swallow the yawn, and looked round guiltily to see if any of his comrades had noticed. He was the youngest in the company; it was not long since he had played at soldiers with his younger brothers. Now he was a real soldier, waiting for his first battle to start.

The lad was lonely and homesick, although he had nearly two hundred of his own kin and clan with him in the meadow. The rich pasture, starred with buttercups, and the green woods of Worcestershire were sadly different from the wild grandeur of his Highland home. The quiet Severn was quite unlike the tumbling and singing burns of his native mountains. The long march down England had been exciting, following the skirl of the pipes and the royal standard.

Now, on the very brink of battle, all seemed different. He threw down the stick, put away his knife and stood up to look round. Half a mile or so behind was the walled city of Worcester, with its graceful spires and tall cathedral tower clear in the morning light. In front of him was the river, and beyond it the sun glinted on the steel helmets of Cromwell's soldiers as they, too, waited behind thick green hedges. In the farther distance a squadron of cavalry trotted to take up a position, the horses tossing their heads.

He tried to swallow another yawn of nervousness, and at that moment his Uncle James went up to him.

'What, Johnny, tired so early in the day?' he said teasingly.

'We were up before the dawn, Uncle Jamie,' said Johnny.

'That for a tale!' said his uncle, sitting down at his side. 'I ken well why you yawn, laddie. Waiting beside your arms is the worst part of it. Aye, laddie, there are two hosts of brave men in these fields this morning, many of them veterans of a dozen battles or more, yet I tell you there's a deal of yawning going on!'

'But – do even you feel it, Uncle Jamie?' asked Johnny, astonished.

His uncle nodded his head. 'Yes, Johnny, but it melts away at the sound of the pipes! When they cross that stream in front the Laird will give the word, and shoulder to shoulder we shall go to meet them, to the war music of the pipes and – you'll not be yawning then, my lad! But stay close to me, for I've given my word to your mother to take you back safe to Scotland.'

'Uncle Jamie, we shall win, shan't we?'

'As for that, who can tell? They have the better of us in numbers, thirty thousand to our sixteen thousand, it is said. But we have the better of the ground; a strong citadel behind us, and the rivers at our front. And, Johnny, we have the King!'

'When Cromwell is defeated shall we march to London?'

'Aye, straight to London, Johnny, and a bonny sight it will be to see His Majesty welcomed by his own subjects, with the ringing of bells and the cheering and the firing of royal salutes from the Tower of London. There will be feasting, and rewards, and we shall go home in triumph ourselves.'

Johnny stood up, his eyes shining. He looked back at Worcester and then he said, pointing, 'Look, Uncle, there he is, on the top of the cathedral tower. There is the King!'

'Aye, there's the King,' said Johnny's uncle. 'Puir laddie.'

'Why do you speak of him like that?' Johnny asked.

'Why, because his life has been hard and he only twenty-one years old. The eldest son of the King, the Prince of Wales, his childhood was passed in stately palaces with good learning and careful ways. Then, when he was only twelve he joined his father in the field and lived a restless life in camps and country houses until after five years Parliament prevailed, and it was all over. Then he was hunted down the west country, to the Scilly Isles, and to Jersey until he had to flee in exile to Holland. Now he is back to claim his crown, with his Scottish army and a handful of loyal English. When the sun sets on this day he will know his destiny. Either to go to London in triumph as King, or as a captive, perhaps to die as his father died two years ago, before a gaping crowd, to the beat of muffled drums, by the executioner's axe. 'Tis much, Johnny, for a lad of twenty-one.'

'Then, Uncle, we must prove his right by our Scottish swords!'

'Bravely spoken, Johnny, bravely spoken! But look, something's afoot across the river. It will not be long now. Keep close to me, and waste no blows on breast-plates of steel or on iron helmets!'

Johnny nodded, and looked across the river, where drums had started to roll and the enemy had begun to form into their lines. With a jingle of harness the Duke of Hamilton rode by, followed by his staff. The men in Johnny's company stood up and loosened their swords in their sheaths. Bugles sounded in other parts of the fields. There was a stir of activity, an excitement in the air. Johnny turned and looked up to the top of the cathedral tower again, and swore that, come what might, he would prove his manhood that day.

The King turned his head towards the half dozen men who were with him on the tower. Two of them went forward to join him, George Villiers, Duke of Buckingham, and Henry, Lord Wilmot. The Duke of Buckingham was the King's intimate friend; indeed he had spent his childhood with the royal children. Wilmot was a stolid man of forty, essentially a fighter and notably brave.

'See, at last they are moving on our right,' the King said. 'I thought they'd attack with their left flank first. They are advancing their Foot towards the river.'

They watched the long columns of Cromwell's infantry marching towards the river. They fanned out into their battle lines and mounted officers galloped into position. Standards made points of colour and the sound of trumpet and drum came clear in the still morning air. Puffs of smoke appeared as the Royalist infantry opened fire with their muskets from behind the hedge-rows. From the top of the cathedral tower it was remote and unreal, like a battle with toy soldiers.

'I wish I had ten, or even five, thousand English,' said the King, 'instead of scarce a thousand to support my good Scotsmen! I thought they would rally to me as we marched southward, but they only barred their doors and let us pass.'

'There is a madness in England these days, Sire,' said Buckingham. 'They think all happiness will come if the land is ruled by Parliament alone, without a monarch. It will pass. But now, they are obstinate, as only the English can be!'

'Yet it is sad that I must kill my own people to win their allegiance. They believe they are right.'

'Obstinacy must be cured by harsh means, Sire,' said Buckingham grimly.

'You have shown yourself merciful, sir,' said Wilmot, 'in the general pardon you have published.'

'There were a few exceptions,' said the King, 'among them Oliver Cromwell! Yet, to give the devil his due, I confess he's a superb general.'

'Then, sir,' said Buckingham, 'the greater the honour in defeating him.'

'By your leave, Your Majesty,' said Wilmot, 'I must go to my post below, with my regiment.'

'Yes, the hour has come,' said the King. He turned to the others, the Earl of Shrewsbury, the Earl of Derby, and Lord Levison. 'Gentlemen, to your posts, and God be with you! I shall stay here for a while with the Duke of Buckingham to watch how affairs turn out. When it is time I shall lead the Horse myself.'

'Is it wise, Your Majesty,' said Lord Derby, 'to venture your person in battle?'

'This is no day for caution, James,' the King said with a smile, 'and it is my duty to lead the Horse. There is my brother James safe with my mother abroad, so it does not matter if I fall. So, gentlemen, good fortune!'

The four men saluted and went down the spiral stone stairs of the tower, their armour and heavy boots echoing. The King turned again and leaned on the parapet of the tower to watch the battle, the dreadful game to decide the fate of the King and the future of England.

The fighting was desperate for two hours and more. The sternly disciplined Roundheads fought for their ideal of a land which would be governed by the people through Parliament. The Royalists fought with devotion for their King, true heir to the long line of Kings of England. From the one side came the steady beat of the drum, from the other the wild and romantic skirl of the bagpipes.

Cromwell's Ironsides were the finest fighting troops in Europe, and the Militia, which made up his army of thirty thousand men, were experienced in many a battle during the long Civil War. Gradually the Royalists were forced back, and relentlessly, fighting from hedge to hedge, the King's army fell back towards the walls of Worcester.

'Come, George,' said the King suddenly to Buckingham, 'it is time to use our cavalry. Perhaps the shock of our charge will check them, and we can drive them back to the river.'

They hurried down the stairs and went out to their waiting squires. They put on their helmets and wriggled them into a comfortable position. The King mounted his grey horse and trotted into the cobbled road, followed by his Standard Bearer with the Royal Standard of England. The staff rode behind, two by two, out under the gate-tower into the meadow beyond.

The Royalist cavalry were standing by their horses. As the King rode up there were sharp commands, trumpets sounded, and the men mounted their horses. Swords flashed in the sun as they were whipped from scabbards and the horses whinnied and pawed the ground. The King cantered forward to his position in front of the long line and drew his sword, giving the sign to advance. It was a brave and splendid sight as the thousand horsemen moved forward, equipment jingling and the sun flashing on polished armour.

The trot broke into a canter, and the Royalist Foot opened their ranks to let them through, and cheered them on their way. They broke into a furious gallop and then loosened their reins for the charge, sweeping down upon the enemy, who stood stoutly on the defensive. Then all was confusion and noise; the roar of muskets, the clash of steel, and the yells and cries of men and horses.

Oliver Cromwell, Lord General of England, watched from some rising ground apart, sitting his horse impassively. He snapped his fingers and an aide-de-camp walked his horse forward. Cromwell gave him a brief order and the young officer turned his horse and galloped off to the rear. Soon four squadrons of Parliament Horse came up from their position in reserve and threw themselves at full gallop into the fray.

The young King fought valiantly in his first battle. All knew that this was the climax of the day and fought with the utmost determination. Gradually the Royalists were checked, and yard by yard they were driven back until the tide of battle turned, and they were galloping back towards the city, pursued by the triumphant Roundheads. Only when he saw that the day was lost beyond all hope did the King turn his horse and ride back to the city.

There was confusion at the city gate, where a heavy dray had been overturned across it. The King dismounted and crawled under the dray, mounted another horse, and rode into the city. He stopped in a quiet courtyard and dismounted. Several of his staff joined him.

'Well, gentlemen, what now?' he said.

'One thing only, Sire,' said Lord Derby, 'and that is flight, and quickly.'

'Flight, eh?' said the King. He listened for a moment to the tumult of battle within the city. 'Then we had better take off our armour.'

At that moment a tall Scotsman hurried past, leading a dozen battle-stained comrades. 'This way, my boys,' he shouted, 'through Friar's Gate and we can get at them again!' A youth was with them, his face grimed with sweat, eagerly hurrying towards the battle again.

'Here, boy,' said the King, 'unfasten this buckle. It is stiff.'

The boy stopped, recognized the King, and gaped at him in astonishment.

'Come, hurry, boy,' the King said.

It was Johnny. He went to the King, knelt down, and unfastened the strap. Then he helped the King to take off his heavy cuirass.

'That's better,' said the King, stretching. 'But give me the Garter riband, I'll not leave that behind!'

Johnny handed him the blue ribbon, which he fastened over his shoulder.

'I am sorry, my young friend, to have brought you so far from your home, and to have lost the day. Get away as soon as you can. Travel swiftly and avoid the main roads. Lie up in woods by day and travel by night. God grant you reach the border safely.'

'My Uncle Jamie will get me home safe,' said Johnny.

'Fortunate youth, to have an Uncle Jamie. I wish I had! Here, keep this gauntlet in remembrance of me, and good luck to you!'

'Good luck to you, Your Majesty,' said Johnny, his shyness melted by the King's friendly smile, 'and one day you will come back!'

'Come, Sire,' said the Duke of Buckingham, 'we must not delay.'

The King mounted his horse and rode with the others to the northern part of the city. Johnny stood quite still, the heavy steel gauntlet in his hand, gazing after the tall young man in the buff coat, the handsome King with the friendly smile.

B

CHAPTER TWO

WHITELADIES HOUSE

THE King and his companions dismounted hurriedly at the oak-beamed house which had been their headquarters. While a hurried council of war was held Scottish soldiers kept the enemy at bay in near-by streets, and at the Town Hall a company of English Royalists made a brave but hopeless stand. The Roundheads poured into the city and the streets became battlefields. The citizens listened to the tumult in terror from behind barred doors and closed shutters.

'Well, gentlemen,' said the King, 'what chance have we of rallying our forces in a final attempt to save the day?'

'None, Sire,' said Lord Derby. 'They are scattered and exhausted. We are hopelessly outnumbered.'

'There is but one hope, Sire,' said Lord Cleveland, 'and that is flight to Scotland.'

'Or, perhaps,' said the King, 'to London. If we could get there before they hear of our defeat we might rally the city to our cause.'

The Earl of Shrewsbury shook his head. 'Cromwell has posted a strong force on the road to London.'

'Then we must turn tail,' said the King with a sigh, 'and race Cromwell's men to Scotland.'

'I have ordered that the freshest horses to be had shall be collected at the back of the house, Sire,' said Lord Cleveland.

'Colonel Carless has a squadron of picked cavalry for our rear-guard,' said Lord Wilmot. 'There's not a better man for the task, he will fight them off if they get too close.'

'Then,' said the King, 'it is flight!'

At that moment there was a great commotion outside the house as a number of horsemen rode up. There were shouts and commands, then an imperious knocking at the locked door.

They all stood still. Then unexpectedly the King laughed, suddenly gay in the face of danger.

'Come, gentlemen,' he said, picking up his short red cloak and swinging it on to his shoulders, 'it seems we should be on our way. Let us leave by the back as they come in the front.'

A number of horses were held by troopers in the courtyard behind the house. The King and his companions mounted quickly and set off towards the northern gate of the city. Soon they were clattering through and, once in the open country, set spurs to their horses. It was a misty evening, with rain in the air. Behind them the remnants of the Scottish army began to straggle out from Worcester.

About a mile north of Worcester the road divided, and the cavalcade pulled up to consider which road to take.

'The lesser road would be safer, Sire,' said Lord Cleveland. 'The rest of the army will be sure to take the other, so the pursuit will be hottest there.'

'Where does it lead?' the King asked.

'Through Kidderminster and Stourbridge to Wolver-hampton, sir,' said Lord Derby, 'it was this way I came to Worcester last week.'

At that moment they heard a horse approaching at full gallop. The lords moved their horses to protect the King as a trooper came up.

'A message for His Majesty from Colonel Carless,' he said, 'a strong force of the enemy are in pursuit. Colonel Carless is holding them at the woods half a mile back, but he cannot keep them at bay for long.'

'Thank you, my friend,' said the King. 'Return to Colonel Carless and tell him that we are taking the lesser road at this fork. Give him my thanks for his good service. Come, gentle-men, forward!'

They set off at a good round canter. All day the King had suffered the anxieties of the fateful battle, he had himself

fought hard with the cavalry, and afterwards had only just
avoided capture in Worcester. Yet he was in excellent spirits.
His enemies were behind him and the future was unknown.
It was to be a battle of wits, and in that King Charles had every
advantage.

They rode steadily forward through the dusk and then in
the darkness. They thundered through sleeping villages and
lonely farms. A few miles behind them Colonel Carless was

fighting a masterly rear-guard action. He would find a good
position, post his men to ambush the road, open fire on the
pursuing Roundheads, and hold them up. When they were
deployed to discover what strength they had before them
Carless would quietly disengage his men and ride on to a new
position.

Ahead of him the royal quarry and his fifty companions rode
steadily northwards. Thirteen miles from Worcester they made
a detour across-country to avoid Kidderminster, crossing the
river Stour into the desolate country of Kinver Heath. Here

the trooper who had been acting as guide slowed down and stopped, confessing with chagrin that he had lost his way.

'If this is Kinver Heath, Sire,' said Lord Derby, 'I know a place not far away where Your Majesty would be safe. It is a house called Whiteladies, belonging to Mr Charles Giffard. I hid there myself on the way down to Worcester.'

'Do you know the way there?' the King asked.

'No, Sire, but Mr Giffard is riding with us. He will be able to guide you.'

'Then send for him!'

Lord Derby called Giffard's name and he rode forward through the darkness.

'You want me, my lord?' he said to Lord Derby.

'Yes. His Majesty will rest at Whiteladies.'

'His Majesty will be safe there, my lord. But it is another ten miles, through Stourbridge.'

'Then let us go there,' said the King.

'I'll call my servant, Your Majesty,' said Giffard, 'he knows the by-ways and short cuts and he çan guide us.' He turned in his saddle. 'Francis Yates, hither, man!' he called.

A thick-set man rode up.

'You want me, Master?' he said, in the broad Worcestershire dialect.

'Yes. Lead us to Whiteladies House, Francis, and make no mistake about it!'

'I'll make no mistake, Master,' said Yates. 'I know this country like the palm of my hand.'

'Lead on, goodman Yates,' said the King, 'and set a good pace.'

Yates and Giffard rode to the front and the cavalcade set off again, riding eastwards across Kinver Heath. Soon their horses' hooves were echoing in the silence of Stourbridge. After Stourbridge they rode on, pressing their tired horses forward.

Sixteen miles behind, troops of Cromwell's Horse were leaving Worcester, each commanded by an officer who had been told to search every road and lane, every house and barn, to capture Charles Stuart. Oliver Cromwell had won the battle, which he called the Crowning Mercy. But he had not yet got the greatest prize. His orders were clear and definite: Charles Stuart must be captured.

George Penderel, one of Mr Giffard's servants at Whiteladies House, slept in a little room over the gate-house. Very early in the morning of 4th September he was woken by a loud knocking on the gate below him. He went to the window, opened it, and in the first light which comes before the dawn he saw two figures below him.

'Who be there?' he asked, his voice low because of the sleeping house.

''Tis I, George, your master,' said Giffard. 'Come down quickly and open the gate.'

'But – but I thought you had gone to Worcester, Master, to fight for the King!' said George.

'Never mind that, man. Hurry!' said Giffard.

George Penderel closed the window, pulled on his breeches, and threw a cloak round him. As he hurried along the corridor he called his brother John.

'Wake up, John,' he said as he shook him, 'here be Master come; and by his manner something's amiss. I'll go let him in. You go and fetch brother William from his bed. Be stirring, man.'

George went downstairs and unfastened the gate. He stood aside as Mr Giffard and his companion led their horses inside the courtyard. A dozen others followed and dismounted stiffly. George noticed two things; the horses had been ridden far and hard, and the gentlemen were men of rank. Among them he recognized the Earl of Derby, who had been hidden in Whiteladies the week before. As George closed the gate again he noticed that many more horsemen were waiting near by.

He hurried into the Hall, where Mr Giffard had taken his companions. George kicked the smouldering logs into life and opened the shutters. The Earl of Derby and a very tall young gentleman went over and stood by the fire.

'What news from Worcester, Master?' George asked Mr Giffard.

'There was a battle yesterday, George, and we were defeated.'

'Alas, Master, then our troubles are not over.' George shook his head. Then he asked, 'And His Majesty himself, what of him? Is he safe?'

'He is safe, George,' said Giffard, 'but he is close pursued.'

'May God save and preserve him!' George said fervently.

'Amen to that, my friend,' said a pleasant voice behind him. George turned and saw that it was the very tall young man.

'This, sir,' said Mr Giffard, 'is a servant of mine, George Penderel. He has four brothers, all stout-hearted men and true.'

'I can vouch for that, sir,' said Lord Derby, 'the Penderels gave me safe sanctuary last week. I would entrust my life to them, as indeed I did.'

At that moment two more of the Penderel brothers came up to their master; William, the eldest, and Richard. The tall young man looked at them and then turned and went into the parlour, followed by the other gentlemen.

'This is what you must do,' said Giffard. 'Richard, you are the tallest. Go and fetch your best clothes, a complete set, everything, mark you, and take them to the parlour. Also bring some scissors, for cutting hair.'

'Yes, Master,' said Richard, 'but what is afoot? Who are all these fine gentlemen?'

'Anon, Richard, anon. Hasten to fetch clothes and scissors. And you, George, fetch some food and a jug of sack, and quickly too. William, come with me.'

Richard and George Penderel hurried off and William followed his master into the parlour. Lord Derby came forward.

'Ah, William Penderel. You cared for me and hid me from the Parliament soldiers. I have great faith in you.'

'That you can have, my lord.'

'You will see how greatly I trust you. We are hotly pursued by Cromwell's men. Shortly we shall all ride away, save only one of us. That gentleman by the fireplace I am entrusting to your care. He is – the King!'

William Penderel looked at Lord Derby for a moment, then he turned and looked at the man standing by the fireplace.

'The King!' he said, in amazement. 'His Majesty, here, in Whiteladies House!'

'It is the King, William, and his life is in your hands.'

'I am sorry, Master William Penderel,' said the King, 'to thrust myself upon you in this manner. But we are hard pressed and I must have a hole to hide in.'

William Penderel went over and dropped on to one knee.

'Your Majesty,' he said. 'Thank God that you have come here. We will see you come to no harm, no matter how many come a-seeking you. You'll be safe!'

'I thank you, my friend,' said the King, 'and from what my Lord Derby has told me of you, and from the evidence of my own eyes, I have great comfort in being in your care. So rise, man, let's to business.'

Richard Penderel hurried into the room, carrying a collection of garments, but he stopped and stared in surprise when he saw his elder brother getting up from kneeling.

'Sire,' said Lord Derby to the King, 'we must leave you now. We cannot all find concealment here at Whiteladies. We will ride on, and fend for ourselves as best we may. If we can get to Scotland, perhaps we can raise another army. If not, then we will make our several ways to France.'

'So be it, my friends,' said the King sadly, 'and God go with you all. Have no fear for me. I shall lie here for a few days with these good fellows, and then I'll try to make my way to Wales and thence to France. We must hope to meet in happier circumstances!'

They went up in turn and took his hand; Buckingham and Shrewsbury, Cleveland, Derby, Wilmot, and the others. The

King took off his blue riband of the garter and his jewels and gave them to his comrades. Meanwhile Giffard had called William and Richard aside.

'Give His Majesty these clothes to wear. Cut his hair in the country fashion. Teach him to speak and walk as a country-man. Cromwell's soldiers will search every house, and they will be here soon. Take the King into Spring Copse during daylight, it will not be safe in the house. Remember, both of you, be vigilant and faithful.'

'Have no fear on that score, Master,' said William.

Giffard bade farewell to the King, and went out after the others. The King went to the window and opened the shutters. It was a cold grey dawn, with a drizzle of rain. He watched his friends mount their tired horses and ride out through the gate-way, out into the open where ten thousand determined men would be hunting them. The King listened to the noise of their horses' hooves dwindling in the distance until all was still. He closed the shutters and sat down at the table, resting his head in his hand. He looked forlorn and very lonely.

CHAPTER THREE

THE ROYAL WOODMAN

NEITHER William nor Richard Penderel had the courage to break the King's reverie. They watched him with awe – and pity as well. At last William stepped forward and coughed politely.

'May it please Your Majesty,' he said, 'here be brother Richard with garments our master bade us bring for you.'

Charles looked at William, then at Richard. He came out of his reverie and stood up.

'Your pardons, good friends. I was bemused with long thoughts. But this is no time for day-dreams.' He yawned and added with a smile, 'Though real dreams in a good sound sleep would not come amiss. I confess I am much fatigued. However, let me see your clothes.'

Richard went forward and put the bundle of clothes on the table. 'These are the best I have, Your Majesty. We have no fine clothes here, being but simple folk.'

'I have done with fine clothes for a while,' said Charles.

'Here is a noggen shirt, Your Majesty,' said Richard, holding it out, ''tis only of coarse hemp but it is proper to a country person of humble station.'

'A country person of humble station, yes, that is the part I must play. What else have you? Ah, coat and breeches of green cloth and a leather doublet.'

''Tis doeskin, Your Majesty,' said Richard with some pride, 'though I confess it has had much wear. There are these shoes, which should fit Your Majesty. This hat belongs to our brother Humphrey, he who's a miller.'

'It is an excellent hat, my friend,' said Charles, politely picking up the greasy old hat with the tips of his fingers, 'and

I can tell that your brother Humphrey is a miller from the flour dust in the brim. Now, I will put on these new clothes, and become a new man. No longer Charles the King, but Charles the – the what? Farmer? Shepherd? Miller?'

'Best of all would be a woodman, Your Majesty,' said William, 'it is a calling which takes a man naturally into the woodlands, so there would be no suspicion if you were found in a desolate place.'

'Then a woodman it shall be. And not Charles, neither. New dress, a new calling, and a new name. What shall it be? William is a good name, William Jones. Will Jones the Woodman. Come help me to change my outward appearance.'

At that moment George Penderel came in, carrying a trencher of food and a jug. He put them on the table.

'Master bade me bring victuals, my lord,' he said, 'and I have found what I can in the kitchens. Here be sack, too.' George set out bread and cheese and the jug, and being a talkative young man chattered as he did so.

'The other lords have gone I see, and my lord of Derby with them. Did you see the King, my lord, at Worcester? Think you he can escape? The hunt will be perilous hot, I wager. I fear he won't elude them long, the poor lad!'

'George,' said William Penderel, 'you do talk so! Hold your tongue, man!'

'Why, have I said aught amiss?' said George, looking at their visitor. Then something in the expression of his brothers and in the amused expression of the stranger gave him a clue to the possible truth.

'But – but you're not ...?' he said, looking at Charles with round eyes.

Charles laughed, and then nodded.

'Yes, I am, friend George,' he said, 'and do not marvel! I have been left here by my friends because it is the home of loyal and gallant men.'

George dropped on to his left knee. 'They didn't tell me!' he said, 'else I'd not have let my tongue wag so.'

'Come, get up, my friend,' said Charles, 'you said nothing that was not good for me to hear. And what is more to the point you have brought me food and drink. I am much in need of both.'

The King sat down and ate quickly. Then with the help of the three brothers he changed into the country clothes, and stood before them.

'Will I do?' he said.

'It is a pity Your Majesty is so very tall,' said William. 'Woodmen are more often short and stumpy men.'

'That is a matter I cannot help,' said Charles, 'but if you teach me I will learn to walk with a stoop when we are abroad.'

'Saving Your Majesty's presence,' said Richard, 'there is another matter. Your Majesty's hair is long and handsomely curled. It had better be cut in the country fashion, shorter and rounded.'

'Must I lose my hair, too?' said Charles with a sigh. 'Ah well, better to lose my hair than my head. Come, Richard, you shall be the barber.'

He sat down and Richard picked up the heavy scissors he had brought. He considered the fine dark-brown hair of the King, and at first he snipped it hesitatingly, but soon he gained confidence and the scissors clicked merrily.

'This is like old times,' said Charles. 'Always I had two or three gentlemen of the bedchamber to dress me, and another to trim my hair. But they were no more excellent than you, my friends!'

'We are but rough fellows, sir,' said William, 'but you will find us constant.'

George had been strangely silent since he had discovered who their visitor was. Now he plucked up courage to speak.

'There is another matter, Your Majesty,' he said. 'Your hands are too clean and gentlemanly.'

Charles looked at his hands, and they seemed to him to be dirty enough for any woodsman.

'What do you suggest, George?' he said.

'Your Majesty might rub them in the back of the chimney,' George suggested.

'A good idea,' said William. He began to pick up the hair which had fallen from his brother's scissors.

'May I have some of your Majesty's hair?' George asked.

'You can have it all,' said Charles.

'No, Sire,' said William firmly, 'it must be burned. If they come to search it might be found, and give all away.'

He threw the hair on the fire where it burned up quickly. The King went to the grate and rubbed his hands in the soot at the back. He wiped them on his breeches, put on the hat, and presented himself once more to the scrutiny of the three brothers.

'How does Will Jones the woodman seem now?' he said.

'It is a good disguise,' said William, 'and if Your Majesty can hold yourself less erect, and bow your head a little, 'twill serve.'

'A wood-bill,' said George suddenly, 'he must carry a wood-bill,' and he went out of the room.

'What now?' said Charles. 'It is full dawn, and the world will be astir.'

'Your Majesty had best hide in Spring Coppice, a small wood hard by,' said William. 'One of us shall stay with you, the others shall keep watch.'

George came in with a wood-bill which he gave to the King. 'Hold that in your hand, Your Majesty,' he said. 'It shows your trade and calling.'

'My friends,' said Charles seriously, 'I have only words wherewith to thank you. When happier days come I will reward your loyalty as it deserves, and everyone shall know how you risked your lives for me. But that is in the far future. For now, lead on to Spring Coppice.'

They went out by the back door, crossed the courtyard, and took a footpath which led them to the wood. William and George went off to watch the near-by road and promised to post their brother Humphrey as an additional guard. Richard spent a few minutes instructing the King how to walk with the proper gait of a countryman. He practised carefully and tried also to imitate Richard's slow Worcestershire accent. When the lessons were over they found a clump of bracken behind some bushes and the King sat down, leaning against the trunk of a tree.

'I shall sleep awhile,' he said. 'Yesterday was as hard as any day in my life, and I was in the saddle all night.'

'Do so, Your Majesty,' said Richard. 'I will keep watch.'

The King soon fell asleep, and did not wake up when a fine drizzle of rain began to fall. Richard took off his coat and laid it gently over the King. He stood looking down at him for a few moments, and shook his head sadly. Then he went back to his post.

An hour later a woman's voice called his name. 'Richard! Richard Penderel,' she called. 'Where be you?' She continued calling, gradually coming nearer.

The King woke up, yawned, and stretched. Then he listened to the woman's voice, looked at Richard and Richard looked at him.

'It's my sister, Jane, Your Majesty,' he said. 'She's married to Francis Yates, he who led you to Whiteladies.'

'I remember him well,' said the King, 'but we don't want any women in our secret.'

'Richard,' came the voice, now quite near, 'where are you? Come out and show yourself!'

'Jane's a persevering woman, Sire,' said Richard, 'she'll not give up easily. Perhaps it is better I show myself, someone else might hear.'

'Very well,' said the King, getting up, 'but get rid of her. I'll go deeper into these bushes.'

When the King was hidden Richard called, 'Jane, I'm here. What d'you want?'

'Ah, so there you are!' she said triumphantly. 'So I've found you. Well, where is he?' She looked round her.

'Where is who?' Richard asked innocently.

'The Cavalier gentleman you are hiding, of course! Do you

think I can't put two and two together? Yesterday was the battle of Worcester. This morning before dawn some two-score horsemen were led to Whiteladies by my husband. Now Humphrey and George and you are skulking in Spring Coppice. And you're looking so innocent, Richard, that I know for certain sure that something's afoot.'

'Do you think, Sister, that I'd risk my neck meddling in such affairs?' said Richard.

'You're fools enough for anything, the lot of you! Is it my Lord Wilmot again? Or the Duke of Buckingham? They say he escaped after the battle.'

'Now Jane, be a good lass and get back to your cottage. I'm only watching out, in case anyone comes.'

'Fiddle-faddle,' said Jane. 'Look, I've brought a warm blanket for the poor gentleman, as it's raining, and a dish of milk, eggs, and sugar, fine enough to hearten any wayfarer, be he plain or nobly born.'

The King pushed through the bushes and Mistress Yates grinned in triumph. 'There!' she said. 'I knew it!'

'I am Will Jones, Mistress, a woodman, come to seek work!' said the King, in his newly acquired accent.

'And I'm the Queen of England,' said Mistress Yates, 'come to seek a Cavalier gentleman in hiding from the Roundheads!'

'Cannot you see that I am indeed but a simple woodman, Ma'am? See – my clothes, my accent, my wood-bill?'

'Your clothes, you say!' said Mistress Yates. 'My brother Richard's best coat and green breeches, and my brother Humphrey's hat! And as for your lordship's accent, it is no more of these parts than the King of France's! Nay, my lord – for I take it you are a lord – you cannot fool Jane Yates so easy.'

Charles shrugged his shoulders and smiled. 'Then I am a poor actor, Mistress, and I ask your pardon. But, Ma'am, can you be faithful to a distressed Cavalier?'

'I do assure you, my lord, that I'd rather die than betray you. And see, here is a blanket to protect your lordship from the rain, and a mess of eggs and milk to put heart into you.'

'I am sorry, sir,' said Richard.

'No matter, good Richard,' the King said, 'I warrant your sister is as loyal as her brothers. And as for the blanket, Ma'am, why bless your heart for the thought. And for the dinner you bring me, it is heartily welcome. But, Mistress, why do you look at me like that?'

'But – but it cannot be!' said Jane Yates, looking at him in astonishment. 'Yet the description tallies. "A tall man, about two yards high, his hair a deep brown, near to black"!' She took a pace backwards and looked at her brother. 'Richard, is it true – is this ... *him*, himself?'

'Oh, give over your questioning, Jane,' said Richard.

'Mistress Yates,' said Charles, with a little bow, 'you have discovered my secret. Yes, I am Charles Stuart, at your mercy!'

'You see, Sister,' said Richard glumly, 'you meddled with more than you knew!'

'Oh, Your Majesty,' said Mistress Yates, 'how can you forgive me? The things I said. You see, I didn't know!'

'Come, Mistress Jane, you said nothing that wasn't most appropriate in this my Court! Give me your eggs and milk, and the blanket to sit upon. Do not wonder so. I am the King, hunted in my own realm and, for the time being, gone to earth here in Spring Coppice.'

Mistress Yates laid the blanket on the ground and the King sat down and began to eat the food with a pewter spoon. Mistress Jane watched him, her face full of wonder.

'This is delicious,' said the King. 'Tell me, how did you know I was about two yards high, my hair a deep brown, near black?'

'Such a description has been nailed to the church door, Your Majesty, and cried from the market cross in the town, and from every street corner by the Constable. There is a reward, Your Majesty, of a thousand pounds to he who takes you prisoner, or who tells the soldiery.'

'A thousand pounds, eh? It is a lot of money. And what other news from the outside world is there?'

'The poor Scots soldiers have been passing through, Your Majesty, some of them grievous wounded. They are hiding hereabouts. And the soldiers have come, too.'

'So the hunt is up!' said the King. 'Here, Richard, do you finish this excellent posset, you are as hungry as I am. Come on, man, no ceremony. Mistress Jane, did they say aught about what would happen to those found helping me?'

Mistress Yates hesitated for a moment. 'Yes, Your Majesty, it is – death,' she said.

'Aye, that's the rub,' said the King, 'when I ask for help I ask a man to venture his life!'

'Oh, no, Your Majesty,' said Mistress Yates, 'there be many of us who will conceal you, whatsoever they threaten or offer!'

There was a rustling in the wood and the King slipped quickly into the trees. Mistress Yates and Richard looked anxiously towards the noise. It proved to be Humphrey Penderel, breathless from hurrying.

'Richard, they are coming!' he said. 'A sergeant and half a dozen soldiers. Others are in Whiteladies.' He lowered his voice. 'Where is he?'

Richard jerked his head towards the bushes in which the King was concealed. 'Stay here with me, Humphrey, in case they discover him. You go quickly, Jane!'

'Oh, no,' said Jane, 'I'll stay. You go, Humphrey. Richard, take your knife and mark some trees, as though for felling. I shall sit here.' So saying she sat down where the King had sat, and folded her hands. After a short hesitation Humphrey went off and Richard began to mark a tree with his knife.

Soon they heard the noise of a party of men approaching, scattered into a line the better to search the coppice. Richard listened anxiously. There was a furtive rustling noise as the King moved deeper into the bushes. Mistress Jane sat quite still. Then two soldiers came into the clearing. They stopped when they saw Richard and his sister.

'Sergeant! Hi, Sergeant!' one of them shouted.

'Don't move, either of you,' said the other.

'I have no intention of moving, soldier,' said Mistress Yates.

'What's amiss?' called a deep voice, and a sergeant came into the clearing, shortly followed by several other soldiers.

'These, Sergeant,' said the first soldier.

'Ah. Names?' said the sergeant.

'Jane Yates, wife of Francis Yates, servant to Master Giffard. This is my brother, Richard Penderel.'

'And what are you doing lurking in these woods, eh?'

'My brother is marking trees for felling and I am ...'

'Hold your tongue, woman!' said the sergeant. 'Is your brother dumb? What's your business, friend?' he said to Richard.

'As she said, Sergeant, I'm marking trees for felling. She brought me a posset of eggs and milk.'

'Here's the bowl,' said Jane, holding it out. The sergeant looked at the bowl, and then at Jane and Richard.

'Have you seen any Royalist traitors this morning?'

'I've seen no one but you, Sergeant, and these others that be here with us now,' said Mistress Yates.

'That is so, Sergeant,' said Richard.

'Oh,' said the sergeant. 'Nevertheless we had better search this coppice. You see, Mistress, we have reason to believe that Charles Stuart himself came this way, after he fled Worcester fight.'

Richard glanced anxiously at his sister. She stood up. 'Ah, that might have been it,' she said, nodding her head as at a thought. 'Yes, that might have been he.'

'What do you mean, Mistress?' said the sergeant eagerly. 'Have you seen him? There is a reward of a thousand pounds for his capture, and promotion too I'll wager!'

'Yes, Sergeant,' she said. 'I believe I have seen him.'

'Where, when?' said the sergeant eagerly.

'Well, Sergeant, this morning, just before dawn, I heard the clatter of many horsemen. I went to my window and in the faint light I saw some two score or more mounted men.'

'Yes, yes, go on!' said the sergeant.

'There was one among them, riding to the fore, who was taller than the others.'

'Yes, he is very tall,' said the sergeant. His men crowded round him eagerly.

'I couldn't see him clearly,' said Mistress Yates, 'but I should say his hair was black, and he was doubtless young, and passing handsome.'

'Aye, they say he has the good looks of the devil himself. What happened?'

'Why, nothing. They held a conference and then they set off briskly northwards, that way!' She pointed with her arm.

'Along the road, Mistress?'

'Along the road, and briskly, like I said.'

'That was him! Come, men, we must tell the officer. He'll not escape us. Thank you, Mistress, you have done well! Come, men, to the house.'

They hurried off. Mistress Yates sat down on a log and fanned herself with her hat.

'That was a near squeak,' said Richard.

'That was magnificent,' said the King, looking through the bushes. 'I thought all was up! Bless your ready wit and your clever tongue, Mistress!'

Mistress Yates jumped up and turned round.

'Oh, Your Majesty, I had forgotten you were there!'

'And above all, Mistress, thank you for your description of me! Lord, how those leather-clad fellows made my heart beat! But now, all is well. Richard, I shall compose myself to sleep, comforted by your sister's blanket. Farewell, Mistress, and accept the gratitude of your distressed but most grateful King!'

'God save and preserve you, sir,' said Mistress Yates, with a curtsy. She went away, Richard sat down to watch, and Charles, wrapping himself in the blanket, lay down among the bushes in the drizzling rain, to sleep out the dangers of daylight.

CHAPTER FOUR

WILL JONES SETS OFF FOR WALES

WHILE the King slept fitfully under his blanket in Spring Coppice, too tired to notice the rain, an officer sat at the table in the parlour of Whiteladies House studying a map. He wore leather jacket and breeches, riding boots, a white linen collar which fell over his jacket, and a crimson sash round his waist. He was Colonel Assheton of the Army of Parliament, and as he studied the roads and by-ways of Worcestershire he bit the side of his thumb. A captain stood at his side, respectfully silent. Inside the door two soldiers stood stiffly on duty.

Colonel Assheton drew a rough circle on the map with his thumb nail.

'This much we know,' he said to the captain, 'he's in this area – somewhere. He cannot have gone farther in the time.'

'The woman my men found in the spinney behind the house said the party of horsemen had ridden northwards, sir.'

'I know. She also claimed to have recognized him. But can we be sure? It was only half-light. She may well have been mistaken.'

'There are not many gentlemen of note six foot tall, and dark complexioned withal, sir.'

'It is not easy to tell a man's height when he is mounted. As for his complexion, it was a grey dawn, and she must have been twenty or thirty yards away. I wonder! I wonder!'

A sergeant hurried in and saluted.

'Sir, General Harrison has come!'

Colonel Assheton and the captain looked at each other. The captain straightened his jacket and the colonel got up from his chair. There was a scurry of activity outside, a few brief commands, and the rattle of hooves on the cobbles. In a few moments the general strode vigorously in.

'Ah, Assheton,' he said, 'well, any news?'

'Nothing definite, sir,' said the colonel. 'A woman declares she saw a party of fifty or sixty horsemen ride up to this house at dawn, and then go on northwards. They seem to have been gentry.'

'Did she see Charles Stuart with them?'

'She believes she did, sir. But she may be imagining it.'

'We know he came this way, so she may be right. What have you done?'

'I sent three companies forward, sir, up different roads. I have kept one company here, in case he did not go with them.'

'Good. You seem to doubt the woman's story?'

'One cannot be sure, sir. I decided to wait for you here.'

'I see. Captain, tell them to bring me some food, and some ale. Also provisions for my men.'

'There is nothing left in the house, sir.'

'There will be, if you ransack the place! They always keep

something hidden. This house has a name for being inclined to the rebels, so do not be – fastidious in your search. Get food and drink for me and my men, and quickly!'

'Yes, sir,' said the captain and hurried out. The general paced up and down several times, flicking his riding boots with his whip.

'The Lord General Cromwell has gone to London,' he said. 'I am entrusted with the task of finding Charles Stuart, and, Colonel, I am going to find him! Cromwell called Worcester the Crowning Mercy, and it is an apt description. But it is not complete while this young man is at large. There'll be no peace for this land, no security and no law, until we have him.'

'When you have him, you will – try him as you tried his father?'

'Of course! Without the slightest hesitation, Colonel. I did much to bring about that trial a few years ago, Assheton, and I signed the death warrant joyfully – unlike some faint-hearts! I would do the same again; nay, I *will* do the same again!'

The general looked out of the window at the rain-sodden countryside, and his expression was so resolute that Colonel Assheton almost pitied the young fugitive prince, to have so implacable an enemy.

'This young man is a danger to our land,' the general went on, 'he is a canker in the flesh of our new Commonwealth. There'll be no quietness until he is caught. If he should be allowed to slip through our fingers, to Scotland or to France, then sooner or later he would be back with another army. And the next time the people might not be so steady. Englishmen have a weak affection for a monarch, especially if he be young and handsome. Yes, for the sake of England's peace and freedom we must catch this young prince, and deal with him as he deserves!'

The sergeant came in with bread and cheese and a jug, which he set on the table. The captain followed him.

'You were quite right, sir,' he said. 'They protested that they had nothing, but we found this, and three bags of good flour, two sacks of potatoes, and four hams. They have been taken out to your men.'

'Well done,' said the general. He sat down and began to eat, studying the map at the same time. 'I see you have marked a circle around this house,' he said to Colonel Assheton.

'Yes, sir. Charles Stuart must be somewhere within that area.'

'We will cast our net wider, thus,' said the general, making another circle. 'I have six more regiments coming. Every town and village, every hamlet, shall be garrisoned. I will picket every cross-roads and every lane. Cromwell has ordered me to catch him, and catch him I will. Has the description and the reward been set about?'

'I had a thousand copies printed this morning, sir. They are being read from every market cross and on every village green.'

'Being so tall it is not difficult to recognize him. You can disguise a man but you cannot alter his height. A thousand pounds is a great fortune.'

'And the risk of death by hanging is a strong argument against helping him.'

'And yet,' said the general, raising his mug of ale, 'and yet, there are those so dazzled by royalty, and so infected by the ancient loyalties, that they will refuse the fortune and risk the penalty!' He drank deeply and wiped his mouth with the back of his hand. 'Now, consider it thus, Assheton. If you were in his shoes, what would you do?'

'Try for Scotland, sir.'

''Tis a long march, and we have garrisons across the road. You'd never get there.'

'Then perhaps gamble all on one last throw and try for London?'

'Hopeless. The roads are thick with our men. No, I think I would try to get into Wales. Look, the border is scarce thirty miles away. It is a wild country. He could get to the coast, take ship and – so to France and safety. Yes, I think he might well try to get into Wales.'

'It could be so, sir,' said the colonel.

'So this is what you will do. Ride at once to Kington, here, see? I will send a messenger to meet Blount who is bringing his regiment up, and he will join you there. Close every way into Wales, understand? Every possible route he could take must be stopped. Especially picket every river bridge and ferry.'

'Very good, sir.' Colonel Assheton turned to the captain: 'Tell the men to mount at once. Have my horse brought round.'

The captain went out quickly. General Harrison got up and strolled over to the fireplace. Colonel Assheton tightened his belt and put on his helmet.

'I wonder', said the general, 'where this young man is now!' He picked up the poker and stirred the logs in the fire. They broke into flame. 'Did he come here, to Whiteladies?' the general mused.

He stared into the fire. A curled lock of very dark hair, which had been lying on one of the fire-dogs, fell into the flames and burnt quickly.

'If only I could have a sign,' said General Harrison.

At five o'clock in the evening Humphrey Penderel reported that the soldiers had gone from Whiteladies House, leaving only a small detachment at the near-by inn. Even though the soldiers had gone it was not considered safe to go back, so they went to Richard Penderel's home, Hobbal Grange, instead. They walked through the woods carefully, with the three Penderels, Richard, George, and Humphrey, and Francis Yates keeping a sharp lookout.

A bright fire was burning in the parlour of Hobbal Grange and the King stood close to it to warm his hands and dry his damp clothes, which soon began to steam. The room was scrubbed and clean, there were flowers on the chest at the side, and the table was laid with a white cloth. The King had been morose as they came from the woods, but in the warmth and comfort of the room he brightened.

'This is a good welcome you have prepared for me,' he said to Richard. 'My spirits were as damp as my garments, but already I feel better.'

'We are honoured, Your Majesty, to have you a guest in our humble house.'

'I grieve, good Richard, that you and yours should be put to so great a risk on my account. But it will not be for long. I have determined to go to Wales.'

'To Wales, Sire?'

'Yes, for several good reasons. The border is not far from here, scarce thirty miles I think. I have many good friends in Wales who will give me sanctuary. The wild and mountainous country provides good hiding places, and perhaps I can find a ship to take me to France. So I will leave for the border of Wales as soon as it is dark.'

'It wants three hours or more to dusk, Your Majesty,' said Richard, 'so you can rest before the journey. I know a good and a loyal gentleman, Mr Wolfe, who lives at Madeley, this side of Severn, and about nine miles from here. We can make that the first stage and rest there during daylight and continue tomorrow night.'

'Nay, friend Richard, you have done enough. I will go alone.'

'That would not be wise, Sire. I know the by-ways and foot-paths, and I know Mr Wolfe. Pray let me accompany you.' The request was made so earnestly that the King smiled and said, 'I shall be most happy to have your company, Trusty Dick, and I confess I shall be easier in my mind for it.'

At that moment Dame Jane Penderel came into the room, carrying a tray of food.

'Ah, Mother,' said Richard, 'this is Will Jones, a wood-cutter newly come here to seek work. This is my mother, Will,' he said to the King.

'God be with you, Ma'am,' said the King, bowing.

The old lady looked at him, flushed, and made a deep curtsy.

'God save Your Majesty,' she said, 'and I bless God that

He hath so honoured us in making my children the instruments of Your Grace's safety and deliverance.'

The King looked astonished at first, but her speech so touched him that he gravely gave her his hand.

'Come, Ma'am, we thought it was a secret.'

'My sons can never keep a secret from me, Sire,' she said.

'But I am dressed as a wood-cutter and I thought I bore myself as such.'

'Nay, Your Majesty, your disguise could not hoodwink me. See I have made you a dish of bacon and eggs, and new-baked bread. It is humble fare, but it is the best we have.'

'No banquet has ever so tempted me, Ma'am, for I am indeed hungry. You shall see how I value your hospitality by the way in which I deal with it. And come, friend Richard, do you sit down too and eat.'

'I will have something in the kitchen, sir.'

'Sit down, man,' said the King, his mouth already full, 'we want no ceremony.'

Dame Jane sat on a settle at the side of the room and watched her son Richard and the King of England doing full justice to the supper she had prepared. Afterwards she fetched a bowl of walnut juice, and stained the King's hands, face, and neck, so that he looked more the part of an open air man. While this was being done Francis Yates asked permission to speak to the King, and stood shyly inside the door.

'May it please you, sir,' he said. 'You may need money in your pocket. I have a little money put away. It is only thirty shillings but here it is.' With a bow he tipped the money on to the table.

'My friend,' said the King, 'is there no end to the kindness I receive from your family! I will gladly take ten of your shillings, that will suffice. And if God grant me a safe delivery from these trials I will repay you a hundred fold.'

'There is no need of that, Sire,' said Francis, proud to have his gift accepted.

When he was alone the King rested in front of the fire,

gazing into the flames. His mind was busy with memories of the past and hopes of the future. At dusk he made ready to go, bade farewell to Dame Jane Penderel and her sons, and set out with Richard towards Madeley, the first stage of his journey to Wales.

When they had gone a mile they came to a lonely mill at a place called Evelith. It was built by a bridge over the mill-stream, and entered by a gate. As Richard closed the gate it slipped from his hand and shut with a bang. At once a door opened and the miller came out, with a heavy cudgel in his hand.

'Who goes there?' he shouted.

'Neighbours, going home,' said Richard.

'If you be neighbours come forward and show yourselves.'

In the faint light of the lantern inside the mill they saw other men. Richard whispered, 'We must jump off the bridge into the water, sir, and wade across. It is only shallow.'

'Jump, then, I'll follow,' said the King.

Richard put a hand on the parapet of the bridge and vaulted over, and the King did the same.

'Rogues, rogues!' shouted the miller, rushing to the parapet and waving his cudgel.

The water only came up to their waists and Richard waded for the opposite bank as fast as he could. The King, unable to see him in the darkness of the mill-pool, followed the creaking of Richard's leather breeches. They waded out on the opposite bank, startling some sleeping ducks who scurried away with a great noise, and set off across the mill meadow at a brisk trot. They stopped under some willows, breathless and soaked to the skin.

'They don't seem to be following us,' said the King.

'No, Sire,' said Richard, 'nor do I think they can have seen your face. It is lucky it is a dark night. Are you all right?'

'Soaked to the skin, out of breath, and with a stone in one of my boots, but otherwise, friend Richard, I am well enough. Lead on.'

'Follow me closely, sir, for it is a difficult and winding path the next mile.'

'I'll follow you, Richard. That mill-pool was parlous cold, the exercise will warm us up, so – forward briskly.'

The miller stayed on the bridge, looking forward into the darkness. Then he went inside, closing the door. A dozen men, travel-stained and shabby, stood anxiously together.

'Have they gone?' one asked, in broad Scottish accents.

'Yes, they seem to have bolted,' said the miller. 'I thought it was all up with you, my friends. Sit down again, and rest.'

'Were they Cromwell's men, think you?' asked another of the soldiers.

'Sure to have been,' the miller said. 'They are searching high and low throughout the countryside. As soon as you have eaten the porridge my wife is making, you must press on, my friends, towards Scotland. It is not safe here, those two may fetch others.'

'It is good of you, miller, to risk your life for us.'

'Nay, it is little I can do, but that little I do gladly, for the honour of our young King. Poor lad, I wonder where he is.'

'Aye, God grant that he is safely hid,' said another.

'I'll go and fetch the porridge you'll be sorely needing,' said the miller, 'and glory be that we scared off those two Round-heads!'

It came on to rain again as the night set in. The boots the King was wearing were rough country-made ones, and quite unlike the boots of skilled workmanship to which he was accustomed. Soaked from wading through the mill-stream, wet from the steady rain, and with sore feet he toiled on, un-complaining. Once when they rested in the scanty shelter of an oak-tree the King sighed.

'Be of good cheer, Your Majesty,' said Richard quickly, 'we shall be at Master Wolfe's house within the half an hour.'

'Forgive my sigh, good Richard. I am not yet accustomed to being the quarry of such a devilish hunt. I shall grow used to it. There must be a sort of pleasure in it, if only one sees it aright. And there is comfort in this rain, it must damp the ardour of my pursuers as much as it damps us! Come, lead on to the house of this good Master Wolfe.'

When they reached Mr Wolfe's house they stopped for a council of war.

'That is the house, Your Majesty,' said Richard.

'Do you go, Richard, while I wait here under this tree. Ask if he can take a gentleman from Worcester fight, sore pressed by Parliament. Say only that I am a person of quality.'

'Very good, Your Majesty,' said Richard, 'do you stay in this dark corner in case soldiers are there.'

Richard went to the house and knocked at the door.

'Who is there?' asked someone from an upstairs window.

'It is I, Mr Wolfe, Richard Penderel of Hobbal Grange.'

'One moment.' Soon there was the noise of bolts being drawn and the door was opened to show an old bent gentleman in a velvet gown, holding a horn lantern so that it shone on his visitor.

'I have come to ask your help, Mr Wolfe,' said Richard, 'I have with me a gentleman of quality, who has escaped from the battle of Worcester. Can you afford him hiding for tonight and tomorrow?'

'I am sorry, Richard Penderel,' said Mr Wolfe, 'you know where my heart lies in these matters. But twice today the soldiers have searched my house. There are two companies of the Militia quartered hard by, and they are zealous in their searching.'

'But Master Wolfe, this gentleman is a person of rank, sore wearied with his travels, and close beset with the enemy.'

'I am sorry for it, my friend, but it is too dangerous. I dare not do it for any man, whatever his rank, unless it were the King himself, of course.'

Richard hesitated for a second, looking away at the shadows

under the tree where his companion stood. Then he stepped closer to Mr Wolfe.

'Mr Wolfe, it is the King who is with me!'

The old gentleman stepped back in surprise.

'The King? His Majesty, with you, here?'

'His Majesty is waiting to know your answer.'

'Fetch him at once, Richard. Why did you not say so before!'

Mr Wolfe held his lantern high the better to see the King when he went into the house, but peered at him more closely when he saw the dirty-faced unkempt young man in the dress of a poor countryman. Then he collected himself, and bowed low.

'You are very welcome, Your Majesty,' he said with some emotion, 'and I consider myself singularly honoured to be able to afford you some small shelter.'

'Master Wolfe,' said the King, 'I do not want to put you in danger by my presence. If we can but rest here an hour or so I will be on my way.'

'Nay, Sire, you must stay here. I count the risk a blessing. But alack that Your Majesty should be brought to this sorry pass, dressed as a humble countryman, and a fugitive in your own realm! Come to the inner room, there is a bright fire and cold meat on the side-table.'

The old gentleman led the way, shaking his head sadly at the sight of the King in such a poor state. He kicked the logs in the hearth into a blaze, and the King sat down in the tall-backed chair in front of the fire with a sigh of relief. Richard took his boots off for him and peeled off his hose. Mr Wolfe hurried out and returned with a bowl of warm water and towels, and the King sat relaxed with his eyes closed while his feet were bathed and dried. Then he ate the cold meat and bread put before him, and drank the wine Mr Wolfe fetched, the best bottle he had in the house.

'It is dangerous to stay here, Sire. The soldiers know my Royalist sympathies, and they know too that I have hiding places, made for priests in the old days.'

'If you can find me some hole to lie in, good Master Wolfe,' said the King, 'so long as it be dry, I shall be mightily content. But rather than put you in jeopardy of your life, we will go on and seek another place.'

'No, Sire, no!' said Wolfe. 'I have a barn full of hay. You can lie safely there, so long as you are still and silent.'

'That will be all I need. Tomorrow at dusk I shall leave you, with the gratitude of a King – a King in sore distress. I am making my way to Wales.'

'To Wales, Sire!' said Master Wolfe.

'Yes, to Wales, where I shall find good friends and safe country to hide in.'

'Alas, Sire, it is not possible. They have picketed every bridge over the Severn, every crossing place is guarded.   The ferries are under guard, and every boat is taken!'

'So! They are very thorough! Is there no way to slip across the Severn?'

Wolfe shook his head. 'Mounted troops came this evening, and put a guard on every crossing!'

'So, friend Richard,' said the King sadly, 'our journey has been in vain, and I imperil this good man to no purpose!'

'Come, Sire,' said Richard, 'do not be downcast. A good sleep in the hay and a safe hiding place is much gained. Tomorrow things may seem better.'

'You are a good fellow,' said the King. He filled his glass again and drank the wine appreciatively. Then he stood up. 'Master Wolfe, I will avail myself of your hospitality.'

'This way, Sire. I have two good plaids here in which you can wrap yourself. I will bring you breakfast in the morning, when it is safe. We will go quietly, so that my household will not know you are here.'

They went out of the house by a back door, crossed a yard, and Mr Wolfe unbarred and opened the heavy door of the barn. It smelt sweetly of fresh hay, and by the light of Mr Wolfe's lantern they saw it stacked at either end of the barn. Richard and Mr Wolfe pulled handfuls away until a cave was made, and there the King and his companion lay down. Mr Wolfe tossed hay lightly in to close the opening, and with a whispered good night, closed the great door.

'What is that rustling noise, Richard?' the King asked after a while.

'Rats, Your Majesty.'

'Oh, only rats! Let us hope they will respect a truce. If we do not disturb them, perhaps they will not bite us! Good night, friend Richard. The hay smells sweet, it is warm and, I hope, safe.'

'Good night, Your Majesty,' said Richard, settling himself in the hay with his head pillowed in his arms.

Soon they fell asleep, buried in hay, in the company of the rats.

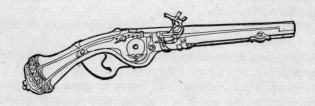

CHAPTER FIVE

BOSCOBEL OAK

THE rats duly observed the truce, and although they investigated the two new inhabitants of the barn from time to time, and made a deal of noise going about their own business, the King and Richard slept tolerably well. In the morning Mr Wolfe brought breakfast, and the news that soldiers were uncomfortably in evidence in Madeley. With their mid-day meal came more news.

'My son, Thomas, has come home safely, Sire,' said Mr Wolfe with great excitement. 'He was captured after the battle and taken prisoner to Shrewsbury. But after an examination and a fine, he was released.'

'Thank God that one good man has survived the battle without harm,' said the King. 'I would speak to him, and thank him.'

'He will be here this evening, Sire. I sent him off at once to find out if there is any chance of crossing the Severn tonight.'

The afternoon passed slowly. The door was kept closed and the only light came through cracks in the wooden walls of the barn. It was a tedious time of waiting, and it was with relief that they heard someone approaching in the early evening. The King and Richard hid in the hay, in case it should be soldiers, but came out gladly when Mr Wolfe softly reassured them. The young man with Wolfe looked with astonishment at the two men who emerged from the hay. Richard Penderel he knew, but the other, dirty and ill-clad, with hay in his hair and sticking to his shabby clothes, bore but little resemblance to the splendid young man in shining armour at Worcester.

'Oh, Sire!' he said with anguish, as he fell on one knee, 'how can this be!'

C

'Come, rise, Master Wolfe,' said the King, with his pleasant smile, 'I apologize for my poor appearance. The times are somewhat out of joint. I am glad to see you safe returned from Worcester. What was your company?'

'I served with Sir Richard Hartley, Your Majesty, we were in Fort Royal, and were sadly over-run.'

'Not before you gave a fine account of yourselves. Did Sir Richard come safely from the fight?'

'No, sir, he was killed.'

'Alas, another good and loyal gentleman lost to me.'

They were silent for a moment as the King stood with his eyes downcast. Then he sat down on a pile of sacks and stretched his arms.

'But to the present. What chance is there of crossing the Severn tonight?'

'It is as we feared, Your Majesty,' said Mr Wolfe. 'Thomas has ridden north and south for five miles each way, and always it is the same. They have every crossing-place guarded.'

'They question everyone,' said Thomas, 'and most closely. They are determined that none of our people shall escape that way.'

'So it is no good!' said the King. 'If they are so zealous over my friends, how sharp they would be to take me! Richard, my friend,' he said, turning to Richard Penderel, 'we must retrace our steps. Perhaps we shall hear news of Lord Wilmot. He was to hide near to Whiteladies.'

'We had better go to Boscobel, my brother John's house, Sire,' said Richard. 'It is a remote place, and should be safe.'

'I am sorry, Your Majesty, that we cannot afford you safe hiding,' said Mr Wolfe, 'but we are beset by Roundhead soldiers and the Militia.'

'You have done me splendid service, Master Wolfe, and I shall not forget it.'

'Thomas here shall bring you supper, Sire, and you had better lie low here until it is dark.'

Mr Wolfe and his son bowed and went out, and the King

and Richard sat disconsolately together in the dim light of the barn. They were silent, and the King became sadly dejected. The chance of getting into Wales had raised his hopes; now the thought of plodding back the way he had come depressed him.

They set out on the journey back to Boscobel at eleven o'clock, when darkness had fallen. Mr Wolfe and his son Thomas accompanied them for the first mile, and when the time came for them to part they kissed the King's hand.

'I thank you both for your kindness,' said the King. 'What is your crest?'

'It is a demiwolf, Your Majesty,' said Mr Wolfe.

'Then in remembrance of this occasion I add to it the Imperial Crown. If it happens that I am restored to my own, you shall receive a Royal Warrant from the College of Heralds. I shall remember you in other ways, too.'

'The addition to our crest is reward enough, Sire,' said Mr Wolfe. 'It will be a reminder to my son's sons and their sons after them, that we were honoured with Your Majesty's trust this day.'

'My safety depends on my faithful friends, such as you. God be with you, my friends.'

'God bless you, sir,' said Mr Wolfe.

Father and son watched the King and Richard walk away into the darkness. Already the King was limping, for the rough boots pinched his feet, still sore from the previous day's march.

'The King of England!' said Mr Wolfe, 'limping through the darkness along rough foot-paths, with ten thousand men hunting him! And he is a good young man. This poor unhappy realm!'

'Even in those clothes, Father, he has majesty! Englishmen seem to have taken leave of their senses!'

'One day they will return to them, and then, perhaps, he will come into his own again.'

'Amen, Father!' said Thomas.

They stopped by a brook after an hour, and Richard filled his horn drinking-cup and gave it to the King.

'Thank you, Richard,' he said. 'How quiet it is! Not a soul seems to be stirring in the whole world! Everyone is abed, save the sentries standing on watch for my friends and for me. And I have no bed, and no home!' He sighed and took off his boots to bathe his feet. There was a silence between them until the King said, 'It might be best to end it all, my friend!'

'What do you mean, Sire?'

'Give myself up, Richard, and end it all.'

'No, sir! No, never! You mustn't think of that!'

'It is hopeless, Richard, and I imperil my friends. It might bring peace to my troubled land. Perhaps I could make terms with Oliver Cromwell, he might spare my life and let me go – if I swore not to try to come back.'

'Noll Cromwell dare not do that, sir,' said Richard. 'I'm but an unlearned countryman, but it seems to me he'd fear that others would try to raise the people in your name. He'd have to – to put you out of the way!'

'Yes, I suppose he would,' said the King thoughtfully. 'But would that be so very hard to bear? I have the example of my father. Perhaps I could show the dignity he showed, and afterwards, Richard – there would be peace.'

Again they fell silent, the King with his own sombre thoughts, Richard Penderel grieved and sore for him. 'The King's Majesty,' he thought, 'the splendour of his boyhood and the greatness of his birth, and now he is sitting by a brook with swollen and sore feet, considering death.'

'Come, sir,' said Richard, 'this is no way to talk. Soon we shall be safe by a good fire, with a milk posset to drink and food to eat. We shall get you safely away. One day your fortune will change, and the people of this land will want the good old days again, a king in London and dancing on feast days, and fairs and merry-making and less of the solemn gentlemen and their many laws. Let me bind your feet with my neckerchief, it will ease them.'

He tore his neckerchief into two strips, dipped it in the brook, and tenderly bound the King's swollen feet. The King stood up and looked about him.

'You think I should go on then, Richard?'

'I know it, Sire. Come, they have not caught you yet, nor shall they!'

'So be it, Trusty Dick, I'll not think again of surrender. It may be I shall have no choice in the matter, but I'll not help them, that I promise you!'

They trudged on, and Richard tried to keep up the King's spirits by telling him tales of the countryside through which they passed and of the people who lived there. Then he asked the King about his own boyhood and the great occasions he had witnessed when he was the Prince of Wales, son and heir of the King of England. The King appreciated his companion's kindly efforts, and did his best to show his gratitude by assuming a more cheerful air.

When they came to the Evelith Mill they stopped to consider how best to get past without rousing the miller.

'We cannot risk alarming that fiery miller again,' said the King. 'We must cross the river lower down.'

'It is deep, Sire,' said Richard, 'and I cannot swim.'

'I can swim well enough for us both, I will see you across. We'll go to the right, over that field, and inspect the river.'

Richard did not like the idea at all, but the King took the lead and Richard had to follow. They got to the river and walked along the bank. It looked deep and dangerous in the darkness.

'Here is a place,' said the King. 'I'll go in first, and you follow me and take my hand.'

'Are you sure it is safe, Sire?'

'Quite safe, Richard.'

Without another word the King waded in, and gasped at the coldness of the water. By good fortune it only came up to his chest, and he held out his hand for Richard who, closing his eyes and saying a hurried prayer, waded in as well. Step by step, feeling his way carefully, the King crossed to the other bank and they scrambled up safely.

'There,' said the King, genuinely cheerful for the first time that night, 'we are across. Now do you lead the way to Boscobel.'

It was three o'clock in the morning when they came to the old black and white half-timbered house. The King sat down under a tree while Richard went on ahead, to make sure that it was safe. The King waited; wet, cold, and anxious. Soon he saw two figures approaching and he stood up, ready to make a dash for it if they were not his friends.

'It is I, sir,' said Richard softly. 'All is well, and I have brought you a friend.'

'A friend?' said the King, looking up at the stranger.

'Lieutenant-Colonel William Carless, Your Majesty, a fugitive from Worcester fight,' said the newcomer formally, standing at attention.

The King stood up and took his hand. 'Colonel Carless,' he said, 'were you not in command of the rear-guard which kept my pursuers at bay after the battle?'

'Yes, Your Majesty.'

'Then I am happy indeed to see you to thank you for your good service. You see me wearing strange clothes, and with an assumed name, footsore and not a little weary, but, Colonel, I am free! They have not got me yet!'

'Nor will they, Sire, if we can do aught to prevent them.'

'Lord, how rich I am in good friends,' said the King.

'There are no soldiers in the house, Your Majesty,' said Richard, 'though there are plenty about. But I think it is safe to go in.'

'Then lead on, good Richard. Come, Colonel Carless, I am indeed happy to have your company.'

Inside Boscobel House, John Penderel and his wife, Joan, received the King, and took him to a warm parlour where supper was laid on a table in front of the fire. Richard Penderel took off the King's boots again, and his stockings, and Mistress

Joan brought warm water and salves, and bathed and dressed his sore feet. While the King ate they discussed the plans for the next day.

'There is no safety in the house in day-time, Your Majesty,' said Carless. 'You had better come with me into the wood at the back. I spent all day there, in a particularly bushy oak-tree.'

'In a tree!' said the King. 'I have lurked in a wood, and hidden in a barn, and it will be a change to perch in a tree. Is there room for the two of us?'

'Plenty of room, sir, and the concealment is complete. Indeed, I had soldiers searching the wood below me!'

'So be it, we will roost in your tree. I wonder if any of my friends are in the neighbourhood – the Duke of Buckingham, Lord Derby, or Lord Wilmot?'

'We have not heard of any of them being near, sir,' said Richard, 'but tomorrow I will go to Wolverhampton and see if I can learn anything about them. I shall meet many friends in the market, and perhaps someone will have news.'

'A good plan,' said Mistress Joan, who was watching the King with a sort of wonder, 'and I have another idea. Let Humphrey go to the Roundhead garrison to find out what he can there. The enemy's camp is the surest place for news.'

'Humphrey to go to the Roundheads, wife!' said John Penderel. 'Would not that be dangerous?'

'Not if he goes on a reasonable errand. We owe twenty shillings to Edward Martin, who has been taken for the Militia. Humphrey can take the money to the captain, and once there use his ears and his wits.'

'Brother Humphrey is just the man for that task,' said John, 'he is as sharp as a weasel. The rest of us will act as scouts about Boscobel Wood.'

'Sh!' said Joan softly, 'see, His Majesty has fallen asleep.'

Soothed by the warmth of the fire and good food, with his aching feet eased by the bathing, King Charles was fast asleep in his chair.

'Leave him, poor young man,' said Joan. 'Post yourselves to keep careful watch. He can sleep until dawn, and then we must rouse him to take him to the safety of the wood.'

They tiptoed from the room. John Penderel pulled up a stool and sat outside the door, one hand on the hilt of his sword, and the others disposed themselves to be able to hear the approach of any strangers. All was quiet.

Half an hour before dawn they woke the King. He put on his stockings and boots, drank a bowl of hot milk, and went out with Colonel Carless and John Penderel into the near-by wood. The colonel carried two cushions and a short ladder and John Penderel carried a basket of food. They went to a certain oak-tree in the middle of the wood, where the colonel had spent the day before. The colonel climbed the ladder first and the King followed him.

The middle of the tree was fairly clear, but the strong branches, thick with leaves, provided a complete screen from the ground below. John Penderel passed up the basket of food and took away the ladder and hid it behind some bushes. Then he trod out the marks it had made on the ground.

'I shall be within hailing distance, Colonel,' he called softly, 'and if there is cause for alarm I will make the same call as yesterday.'

Colonel Carless poked his head through the branches and nodded and John went away.

'I am familiar with the arrangement of the branches, Your Majesty,' the colonel said. 'Yesterday I was passably comfortable sitting here with my legs that way. I suggest that I sit like that and you lie with your head on my lap.'

'I am your guest, Carless,' said the King, 'in your house, so arrange the accommodation as you think best.'

They soon settled themselves comfortably, with the King's head on the colonel's lap. From time to time the colonel suffered from pins-and-needles in his arm, and as the King was soon asleep he had to suffer it as long as he could. The sun

was hot and the flies were troublesome, but for several hours there was nothing else to disturb them.

It was some time in the middle of the morning that Colonel Carless heard John Penderel's warning cry, an excellent imitation of a dove. He pinched the King's arm to wake him, and they both sat up, alert and very quiet. Soon they heard men approaching and a sergeant and some soldiers came into the clearing.

'There's no one in this wood, Sergeant,' one of the soldiers said. 'I think we are wasting our time.'

'It's not our duty to think,' said the sergeant. 'We are ordered to search this wood and search it we shall. But we can take our ease for five minutes in the shade of this tree.'

'This is a wondrous old tree,' said another soldier, looking up into the branches. 'What kind is it, Sergeant?'

'It's an oak-tree,' said the sergeant, 'but don't you bother your head about nature, we've stern duty to perform. There are Scottish fugitives about these parts and a wood like this is just the place to find them.'

'Is it true, Sergeant,' said another soldier, 'that the rebel Charles Stuart has been taken?'

'Aye,' said another, 'so I heard this morning. It seems he was found hiding in a church dressed as an old apple woman, near Wolverhampton.'

'It's not announced officially,' said the sergeant. 'There have been a score of rumours about him being caught these past two days.'

'A thousand pounds reward, that's what Parliament's paying,' said another soldier. 'We'd be rich all our days.'

'The reward isn't for soldiers,' said the sergeant. 'It's our plain duty to apprehend him as an enemy of the realm. The reward is for ordinary folks who give him up. But that's enough of your chattering. Sit quiet, for if there's any of those Scottish rebels about they'll hear you. So sit quiet!'

The King had grinned delightedly at Carless as they listened to the conversation below them. Then they became alert and turned their heads to listen in the other direction. There were soft and furtive noises of persons approaching. The King moved a little on his branch, taking care to make no noise, and parted the twigs in front of him.

Two men were coming towards the oak-tree, moving with the greatest caution, and flitting from tree trunk to tree trunk. From their clothes, ragged and travel-stained, it was obvious that they were from the King's Scottish army. They were going straight towards the soldiers.

Moving his hand very warily the King picked some acorns and as the men came nearer he opened the twigs wider, took careful aim and threw an acorn at the tall man leading. It missed, but the second one hit him on the face. He stopped, looked up, and saw a face looking down at him from the mass of leaves of the oak-tree.

The King held up a warning finger and then made a series of signs which the other quickly understood. He signed to his companion to take cover behind a tree, tiptoed across to another tree and peered round, saw the soldiers, and raised a hand in salute and thanks to the man in the tree. Then he turned to his right and, waving his companion forward, slipped noiselessly through the trees.

Five minutes later the two Scotsmen stopped and sat down, and the leader took out half a loaf of bread and divided it in two. The other, who was not much more than a boy, ate hungrily.

'Uncle,' he said, 'that man in the tree, have you seen him before?'

'Not to my knowledge, Johnny, but he was a good friend. We would have walked straight into those soldiers if he hadn't warned us.'

'I've seen him somewhere,' said the boy, 'though I can't think where.'

'He was some soldier at Worcester, perhaps.'

'Yes, Uncle, it was someone in our army. But – I don't know who.'

'Well, don't worry about it. We've many miles to do this day and I only hope our luck stays with us as it has so far. Not least the warning from the stranger in the tree.'

When the soldiers had gone and it was safe to speak Colonel Carless said, 'That was a risk, Sire, warning those two soldiers.'

'It was a risk I am heartily glad I took. I was glad to be able to warn two of my poor soldiers who are so far from their home in the midst of a hostile country. But when I saw the younger of the two, then I was especially glad I could help them.'

'Why so, Sire?'

'Did you not notice that the boy, for he was little more, was carrying something? In spite of his hardships he was carrying a steel gauntlet. It was mine, Carless.'

'Yours, Sire?'

'The lad helped me to take off my armour in a street in Worcester when the day was lost. I gave him one of my gauntlets as a remembrance. He still has it. I pray they make their hazardous journey safely.'

'The elder man had a shrewd and intelligent look. They moved through the trees with the ease and silence of wild animals. I think they will outwit Cromwell's soldiers, Sire.'

'From the bottom of my heart I hope so, Carless! What a sad business this is!'

'Come, sir, there will be a happy delivery for you, and for them too perhaps.'

'Perhaps,' said the King with a sigh. 'But let us think only of the present. What is there in that basket? Let us eat in our tree, and then perhaps sleep awhile, and so pass the day.'

CHAPTER SIX

THE YOUNG LIFEGUARDS

When dusk fell the King and Colonel Carless went back to Boscobel House, where Richard Penderel had reported that he had not only discovered where Lord Wilmot was hiding, but had seen him.

'Well done, Trusty Dick,' said the King, delighted with the good news. 'Tell me about Henry Wilmot.'

'When he left Whiteladies, Your Majesty, he tried to make his way to London but found the road so infested with soldiers that he had to go to earth. He went to Moseley Hall, nine miles from here, the home of Mr Whitgreave, and was hidden in a secret room they have. Yesterday he went to Bentley Hall, which belongs to Colonel Lane. He hopes to go to Bristol and so to France.'

'Splendid! And you saw him?'

'Yes, Sire, and he was greatly relieved to know that Your Majesty is safe. He is returning to Moseley Hall tomorrow, and it is hoped that you will go there tomorrow night, where you can be safely hidden while new plans are made.'

''Faith, Trusty Dick, you have lightened my heart. Henry Wilmot is an old friend, a good companion and admirably resourceful.'

'I, too, have some news, Your Majesty,' said Humphrey Penderel. 'I went to the headquarters of the troops here on the pretext of taking twenty shillings owing to Edward Martin. I saw the officer there, Captain Broadway.'

'He used to be a heel-maker,' said John Penderel. 'He's a pompous man who has risen to captain's rank in the war.'

'Many have risen in rank during the past nine years of war,' said the King, 'and many have fallen! However, what did you discover, friend Humphrey?'

'I found that they know Your Majesty went to Whiteladies, and must be somewhere in this district. They questioned me closely.'

'And learned nothing, I warrant,' the King said.

'I managed to seem quite innocent, Sire, and they seemed to believe me. Else I would not be here.'

'So they know I am hereabouts! They will not slacken their endeavours to find me.'

'It is a good thing, Sire,' said Colonel Carless, 'that you have a place to move to – if Moseley Hall is really safe.'

'Master Whitgreave is a most loyal gentleman,' said Richard. 'He served throughout the Great Rebellion and lost most of his fortune for Your Majesty's father. His house is large and has most cunning hiding places. It seems also that Lord Wilmot and Colonel Lane have a plan for enabling Your Majesty to travel safely to Bristol.'

'Come,' said the King, 'the future seems brighter, and if my enemies seek me diligently, then we must be more cunning to outwit them. Now I am hungry, what is for supper?'

'We have killed a sheep, Sire,' said William, 'for we dared not buy mutton in the market as it might arouse suspicion. How would you like your mutton dressed?'

'Mutton,' said the King, 'excellent! Bring up a hind quarter, and a frying pan, and butter. We will make Scotch collops. I will cook them myself, with Colonel Carless here as my assistant. It is a famous dish. Then to bed, and tomorrow night I will go to Moseley Hall, and so continue this strange journey. So, fetch the mutton, the frying pan, and butter.'

The brothers hurried from the room and the King rubbed his hands together, in anticipation of his supper. Colonel Carless marvelled at his good spirits.

'Carless, my friend,' the King said, poking the fire in preparation for his cooking, 'I begin to have real hope of winning my freedom. You must make your own way to the coast, for there must not be too many with me. We will meet in France. Ha, here is our supper!'

While the King and Colonel Carless cooked the Scotch collops at Boscobel House, three boys sat on the window seat of their bedroom at Moseley Hall, nine miles away. They were in their night-shirts, and indeed, they should have been in their beds. But there had been much excitement at Moseley Hall in the past two days and they had a great deal to talk about. The two eldest were cousins, both nephews of Mr Whitgreave; Tom Palyn, a boy with freckles, and Frank Reynolds, who was dark and clever looking. The third, younger than the other two, was Sir John Preston. He was staying at Moseley Hall for safety. His father, a baronet, had been killed fighting for King Charles I in the Civil War, and his mother had sent him to her friend, Mr Whitgreave, under an assumed name. He was a sturdy boy with a cheerful look to him.

There was only a couple of years between the ages of the three boys and they were good friends, enjoying occasional tiffs and tussles.

'So the excitement is all over!' said Frank Reynolds.

'Yes, we'll settle down to the old time-table,' said Tom. 'Father Huddleston will be back on duty. Latin verbs before breakfast, sums in the morning.'

'And French conversation and Pythagoras before dinner,' Frank added. 'And we haven't got to worry about the Round-heads coming. It's all over.'

'I wonder,' said John cryptically.

'What d'you mean?' said Tom.

'Why are you looking knowing like that?' said Frank.

'I just said "I wonder",' said John. 'You see, I overheard something this evening. I didn't say anything to you two because it didn't seem fair, hearing your uncle and Father Huddleston talking by accident.'

The other two boys stared at John.

'You're making it up,' Frank said.

'All right, I'm making it up. Then I'll go to bed.'

'Wait a minute,' said Tom, 'tell us what you heard.'

'Frank says I didn't hear anything. He says I'm making it up!'

Tom got hold of John's arm and twisted it, just enough to begin to hurt.

'I think you do know something. So you'd better tell us! Or else ...' He gave John's arm a further twist.

'Ow, let go!' John wrested his wrist free and butted Tom in the chest, and a brisk scuffle ensued until Frank pulled them apart.

'Stop it!' said Frank. 'Someone will hear you! That's better. Now, John, what's this you heard?'

'Oh, very well. Only I do feel rather mean, as I overheard it. I went to put away the Backgammon board and Father Huddleston's study door was open. I heard what your uncle was saying and I stopped and listened for a minute or two. That lord who was hiding here is coming back.'

'Coming *back*!' said Frank.

'But he only went away yesterday,' said Tom.

'If you'll let me tell you what I heard without interrupting you'll understand more. Unless you don't want to know.'

'Go on,' said Tom, 'and don't tease. Or else ...'

'I'm not frightened of you,' said John.

'Oh, stop bickering,' said Frank. 'Now, John, what did you hear?'

'Well, it seems someone else is coming here, tomorrow night. This lord who was hiding here is coming to meet the new one. And from the way they were talking it's someone important. Even talking together Uncle and Father Huddleston were careful not to use any names. But I could tell, by their tone of voice. I think the idea is for the first lord to go away again and for us to have the new one here.'

'Hooray, so there won't be lessons yet!' said Tom.

'And we might have the Roundheads coming, and we can all act innocent and fool them!' said John.

'It may not be so pleasant to have them here,' Frank said seriously. 'They say they give you a bad time if they're suspicious.'

'You mean – torture?' Tom asked.

'I don't know about that, but perhaps,' said Frank.

'I wouldn't tell them anything, whatever they did,' Tom said defiantly.

'That's easy to say,' Frank observed, 'but you don't know what it's like.'

'Neither do you,' said Tom.

'And a good thing we don't,' John said. 'I'm going to bed.'

When they were in their beds Tom said, 'Why don't we ask Uncle who the Royalist gentleman is?'

'He wouldn't tell us,' said Frank. 'If it's someone important who's coming, someone who was near the King, then his life depends on it. The fewer people who know the better.'

'I think we ought to know,' said John. 'They can trust us. There's no harm in asking.'

'Except you will be wasting your breath,' said Frank. 'Good night both.'

'Good night,' said Tom and John, and they all settled down to sleep.

It was tantalizing to have a mystery in the house, to have a great Royalist lord hiding there and to be kept out of the secret. But young people have to be patient with their elders, and put up with being kept in the dark, though they can't be blamed for wanting to find out what is going on, or for trying to find out for themselves.

The next day was outwardly a normal Sunday, with church, Bible reading, and Sunday dinner. It was obvious to the boys, however, that Mr Whitgreave and Father Huddleston had much on their minds. They walked together in the garden, in earnest conversation. A countryman came on horseback and was taken to them at once, and the boys could see that he was being questioned closely. John saw Mr Whitgreave himself carrying a pallet bed upstairs to a garret which was not normally used.

On Monday morning the boys went to the room on the first floor where they worked, got out their Latin books, and sat at the table, waiting for Father Huddleston. The stable clock struck seven but Father Huddleston, most punctual of men where lessons were concerned, did not come.

'You see,' said John, 'I'll wager there'll be no lessons. Only preparation on our own. I'll wager he's here, the new Royalist!'

'I saw Uncle Tom and Father Huddleston, and two others, go out last night, about eleven o'clock,' said Frank. 'I heard the garden door open and I went to the window. I could just see them.'

'Why didn't you wake us?' said Tom indignantly.

'That was a scurvy trick, keeping it to yourself,' said John.

'By the time I'd woken you two sluggards they would have gone into the darkness. Besides, there was no need.'

'No need!' said Tom. 'I like that! Who were the other gentlemen?'

'I think one was Colonel Lane of Bentley Hall; you know, he came here last week.'

'Perhaps the other was the lord who came back,' said John. 'Where did they go?'

'Across the garden towards Moorfield, the field by the bottom gate. I waited at the window but I didn't see them again.'

'They went to meet the newcomer,' said Tom, 'and he's here. I wonder who he can be.'

'I'll tell you something else,' said Tom. 'I went down to the kitchens to get some hot water to bathe my knee. All the servants have been sent out except Cook.'

'Sent out, where?' said Frank.

'I don't know. To different places, on various errands. Cook wouldn't say anything, you know what she is. All she said was

"Ask no questions hear no lies, and shut your mouth because of the flies", but it shows something's afoot.'

'Sh!' said Tom. 'Here's Father Huddleston.'

'Perhaps we'll know something now,' said John.

'Perhaps, and perhaps not,' said Frank.

They all looked hard at their open books and then stood up respectfully when the door was opened. Mr Whitgreave came in with Father Huddleston.

'Good morning, my boys, you may sit down,' said Mr Whitgreave, and he himself sat down on the fourth chair at the table. Father Huddleston closed the door carefully and stood behind Mr Whitgreave. The boys tried to look as serious as they could in the hope that he would confide in them.

'I have something to tell you,' Mr Whitgreave said. 'I have a friend staying here, a Mr Will Jones. He wishes to be left alone, quite alone, do you understand?'

'Yes, Uncle,' said Tom, and Frank and John nodded.

'You need do no lessons today. I have another task for you. The windows of this room look over the park to the main road. I want you to be sentries, taking it in turns to be on duty. If you see any soldiers coming, one of you must run at once to tell Father Huddleston or myself. At once!'

The boys nodded their heads and glanced at each other. This was something quite new.

'If the soldiers come, or indeed if anyone turns into the gate and comes towards the house, you must let us know that. And if you do have to warn us, run, run as fast as you can. You understand?'

'Yes, Uncle,' said Tom. 'Is this friend of yours, Mr Will Jones, a very important person then?'

'He is my guest, Tom, and – he does not want to be disturbed.'

'Excuse me, sir,' said John, 'but could you not tell us more about him? He is a Royalist lord, isn't he, hiding after the King's defeat at Worcester?'

'I have told you all you need to know, John,' said Mr
Whitgreave.

'It is best, John, my boy,' said Father Huddleston, 'not to
worry your head about the matter. If Mr Whitgreave's friend
should be, as you say, an important Royalist officer hiding from
the Roundheads, then the less you know the better. Think
what would happen if the soldiers did come. You might be
questioned. If you know nothing you can tell them nothing.
If you were to know more you would have to make up lies, and
that is not easy. So be content to do as you are told.'

'The duty I have given you is of the greatest importance,'
Mr Whitgreave added, 'and one day, perhaps, I shall be able
to tell you more. Now, to your posts. Tom, you are the eldest,
work out a duty roster. Half an hour on duty in turn is enough,
you will find it a long time to stay on watch. This isn't a game,
it's a matter of life and death.'

The two men went, and Tom wrote down a list of duties,
with himself taking the first turn. They all watched from the
windows at first. There was a perfect view of the road, which
ran straight past the house.

'The question is,' said John, 'who is this Mr Will Jones?'

'Mr Will Jones, of course,' said Tom.

'I wager it's a made-up name,' said Frank.

'When I was coming here my grandmother told me to tell
any soldiers who asked questions that my name was Thomas
Jones,' said John. 'It's just the kind of name you make up.
I bet he's an earl or something.'

'It might be the Duke of Buckingham,' said Frank.

'Soldiers!' shouted Tom suddenly. 'Look, coming over the
hill and marching this way. Frank, go and tell them, quickly.'

Frank hurried out and went clattering down the stairs.

'John, you wait until we see if they turn into the park or
not.'

They watched the soldiers marching down the road, making
a cloud of white dust which hung behind them. An officer on a
grey horse was leading. As they drew nearer to the gate of

Moseley Hall John waited by the door, like a sprinter ready for the start of a race, his eyes fixed on Tom. Frank came back and went to another window.

'No, they're going past,' said Tom, with a note of disappointment in his voice. 'Go and report that they've passed, John.'

John went off and the other two watched the soldiers marching away. When John came back he went up to the others.

'I know where he is,' he said. 'I went to find your uncle and I met him coming down those little steep stairs at the end of the corridor. He told me to speak quietly because Mr Jones was asleep.'

'Then he's in the hiding place up there,' said Frank. 'There's a cupboard with a trap-door in the floor. You go down a short ladder to get to the place. It's ever so small.'

'It's half past,' said Frank. 'My turn to be on duty.' Frank took up his position and Tom came away from the window and sat on the table.

'Tom,' said John, 'let's creep up and have a peep at Mr Jones!'

'We mustn't,' said Tom.

'Your uncle only said he wanted to be left alone. If he's asleep it wouldn't matter.'

'You've got to be here, in case I have to send you with a message,' Frank said.

'If you whistle,' John said, 'we'll hear you, and know what it means. We'll be nearer to Father Huddleston's study, so that doesn't matter.'

'It's a risk,' said Tom.

'Oh, come on, just a peep,' John said.

Tom hesitated for a second or so and then, sorely tempted, said, 'All right, just a peep. Shout or whistle if you see anything, Frank.'

'You'll be in trouble if you're caught,' said Frank, but the other two were already in the corridor.

They crept along to the end and then went up the narrow

steep stairs to the attics. Tom led them into a bare room with low beams and went to a cupboard at the end. He unlatched it and showed John the cleverly concealed trapdoor in the floor. They opened it, stopping in alarm when it creaked, and lifted it right up. There was a short ladder down to a very small cavity, more like a very large box than a room. In the tiny room was a narrow pallet bed of the simplest sort, and on it lay a man in rough country clothes, fast asleep. He had dark hair roughly cut, and a very dark complexion. Tom went down the ladder noiselessly and John followed him. They looked at the man on the bed.

'He's no one special,' John whispered, 'look at his clothes, and his hair!'

'He's handsome, though, and quite a young man.'

'We'd better go, he might wake up.'

'And then he'd *eat* you!' said the man on the bed, opening his eyes. He sat up and looked up at the two boys. 'Who the devil might you be, eh?' he said.

'Oh, we are so sorry,' said John. 'We were just having a look at you.'

'We didn't want to wake you up,' said Tom. 'I'm Tom Palyn and this is my friend, Sir John Preston.'

'Then good day to you, Master Tom, and to you, Sir John. Was your father Sir Richard Preston?'

'Yes,' said John. 'He was killed at the battle of Naseby, fighting for the King.'

'Yes, I knew him. I'm glad to meet you.'

'I'm sorry we woke you up,' said Tom.

'Oh, I wasn't asleep, and you know the saying, "A cat may look at a king"!'

'Oh,' said John with a gasp, 'are you – the King?'

'Are you cats?' the man asked.

'No, I see,' said John with a grin.

'Have you ever seen the King?' the young man asked.

'No, sir, not yet,' said John.

'Not *yet*! What d'you mean by that?'

'I mean we shall see him when he comes back and beats Cromwell, sir, and comes into his own again.'

The man looked at the two boys with new interest.

'And I think the King will be heartily glad to see you two young men,' he said.

'Have you ever seen the King, sir?' said Tom.

'Oh yes; but not face to face, of course.'

'What's he like, sir?' said John eagerly.

'Oh well,' said the dark young man thoughtfully, 'that's not easy for me to say. He's a cheerful person I think. Not really warlike. He prefers a peaceful life with lots of friends, and he likes horse-racing and tennis better than campaigns and battles. I don't think he's serious enough to be a king really.'

'You shouldn't say that, sir,' said John. 'Not about His Majesty, especially now, when he's hunted in his own realm by Cromwell's army.'

'Oh, I'm sorry,' said the young man.

'I wonder where he is now,' said Tom.

'Ah, yes, I wonder,' said the young man. 'With good friends I hope.'

'We had a Royalist lord hiding here two days ago,' said John. 'Is your name really Will Jones, sir?'

'That's what I'm called.'

'Well, we thought you were a lord, perhaps an important one, because of the fuss Uncle made,' said Tom.

'Me a lord?' said the young man. 'Oh no, I'm not a lord.'

'I'm afraid we must go now,' said John. 'Would you please do us a favour?'

'Yes, if I can.'

'Well, would you mind not telling anyone that we came and saw you and talked to you. We'd get into trouble, you see.'

'I promise to say nothing about it.'

'Good-bye, and you're quite safe here,' said John, 'we'll see to that.'

'Thank you very much! Good-bye,' said the young man.

Tom and John lowered the trap-door and hurried back to their room to tell Frank about Mr Jones.

'I wonder who he really is,' said John when they had made their report. 'I'm sure Will Jones is a made-up name.'

'Did you see what fine hands he had,' Tom said. 'They were dirty and stained brown but they were long and slender. And he spoke beautifully.'

'Tom! Frank!' said John suddenly, 'I think I know! But, it *can't* be!'

'What d'you mean?' Tom asked.

'He was only young, about twenty-one. He spoke beautifully and he has a sort of merry look. He's very good looking too.'

Tom stood up and looked at John with his eyes wide open.

'You don't mean that – you think he is …'

John nodded. 'Remember how he looked when you asked him if he had ever seen the King! And who else would speak about the King like that?'

'Are you *sure*?' said Frank.

'Yes,' said John, 'absolutely. It fits exactly, the fuss there has been, the precautions, everyone sent out, us on watch. But, Tom, Frank, the King, the King *himself* in our house with us on guard!'

'And the way we chatted to him,' said Tom. 'Oh lord!'

'I just can't believe it,' said Frank, turning back to look out of the windows. 'Oh, look!' he said in horror, 'a troop of soldiers! Tom, run, run and tell them. And they're coming in the gate! And I wasn't watching! Oh, run, run!'

Tom and John both dashed from the room. Frank watched the soldiers march up to the front door. The officer dismounted and with a sergeant at his side strode to the door and hammered on it. A corporal barked commands to the men and they hurried off, muskets in hand, to form a ring round the house. Then four more officers rode up and dismounted.

Soon the other two came back.

'We've got to sit at the table and write out the subjunctive of *capere*. If they come we are to know nothing about – Mr Jones – or anything else.'

They hurried to the table and set about their task as Latin verbs had rarely been tackled before. They held their breath as they heard the tramp of heavy boots coming up the stairs and along the corridor.

'They've gone past the stairs up to the attics,' said Frank.

'Yes, but they are coming *here*!' said John.

All three began to write the subjunctive of the Latin verb *capere* – which means to capture.

CHAPTER SEVEN

'HAVE YOU SEEN CHARLES STUART?'

JOHN PRESTON was waiting in the gallery for his turn to be taken into the drawing-room to be questioned. Tom had been in, and had come out looking pale and defiant. He had been hustled past John so quickly that there had been time only for a fleeting glance between them. Now Frank was in there; soon he would be brought out and it would be John's turn – unless poor Frank was tricked, bullied, or frightened into betraying their terrible secret.

John wanted to slip away and hide, but the soldier on duty outside the door had his eye on him. John had considered trying to make friends with him, for he very much wanted a friend just then. But one look at the soldier showed it would be no good. He wondered what he should say. He knew that if you are in a scrape the less you say the better. The trouble was that they would make him say things.

Two soldiers came into the gallery. They went to a chest, opened it, and rummaged inside. Then they began systematically to tap the panelling, all along the wall, listening to see if it was hollow, and examining each panel to see if it was hinged or false. John imagined the soldiers upstairs in the attics, peering into that cupboard. Would they examine the floor, and discover the trap-door? Had he closed it properly when he came away? He went to the window and looked out.

It would have been so much easier if they had all been questioned together. John went cold when he realized that if he said something which conflicted with what either of the others had said he could give the secret away. If he blundered he, John Preston, could cause the death of the King of England.

'Steady, my lad!' he said to himself. 'Keep calm, don't say more than you must. Don't lie unless you absolutely have to! Don't talk too much. Look them straight in the eyes and don't show that you are frightened. And try to forget that the K— that Mr Will Jones is upstairs.'

John turned round quickly when the drawing-room door opened. Frank Reynolds came out, accompanied by a soldier who kept a hand on his shoulder. John ran forward, but Frank looked straight ahead of him and went by. His eyes were red.

'Frank's been crying!' he thought, quite astonished. 'Poor old Frank. Well, do what they will, I shan't cry!'

A voice, cold and level, came from inside the room. 'The third child, please.'

'Come!' said the soldier, and John swallowed, collected his thoughts, and with his head up went into the room. He walked up to the oak table which had been placed across the room in front of the big window.

Three officers were sitting on the other side of the table. In the middle was a large strong-looking man with thin untidy hair. On his right was a small narrow-faced man with a bored expression, and on his left a younger man, who was leaning forward with his elbows on the table and his chin in his cupped hand. At the end of the table sat a secretary, writing with a quill on a pad of paper.

'Before we question this child,' said the big man, 'I will ask you again if you have recollected where Mr Whitgreave is?'

John looked round to see who was being addressed and saw Father Huddleston standing by the fireplace.

'I can never recollect what I do not know, Major Southall,' he said.

'You are being most unhelpful,' said Major Southall with a sigh. 'This is Whitgreave's house. We know he is in residence. He has been seen today. And suddenly – he has disappeared!'

'Perhaps he went out, to his farm, to the stables, anywhere. I don't know!'

'I see,' said Major Southall.

John was grateful for this incident. It showed him how Father Huddleston spoke to the officers, quite politely, almost apologetically, but giving nothing away. It was comforting, too, to hear Major Southall's voice. He didn't seem to be at all frightening. John moistened his lips, and when Major Southall looked at him he hazarded a slight smile. He had found that a modest smile often softened the hearts of grown-ups when he wanted something. But Major Southall did not smile back.

'Well, who are you, my boy?' Major Southall said.

'John Preston, baronet, at your honour's service.'

'Sir John Preston, eh? Was your father Sir Richard Preston?'

'Yes, sir,' said John. 'He was killed at the battle of Naseby.'

The officer on the major's left leaned across and said, 'Sir Richard Preston raised a regiment of Horse which served against us throughout the war, sir.'

'Parliament took our estates from us,' said John.

'That is unfortunate, Sir John,' said Major Southall, 'but it was only to be expected, wasn't it? The fortunes of war, you know. You were on the losing side.'

'My father did his duty, sir,' John said quickly, and at once wished he had held his tongue.

'I quite understand, Sir John,' said the major, 'that you and I see that affair from different points of view. However, we are not here to discuss the loss of your estates. I want to ask you some questions about more recent occurrences.'

'Yes, sir,' said John, and again wished he could keep himself from speaking when there was no need.

'I want you to answer my questions truthfully. You know, of course, that it is sinful to tell lies?'

'Yes, sir.'

'In this case it would not only be sinful, but very dangerous for you. And, my boy,' said the major, leaning forward and looking very serious, 'if you *do* lie to us we shall know! And the consequences to you would be very very painful. Do you understand?'

'Yes, sir, of course,' said John, 'but I don't know anything you'll want to know.'

'How do you know that?' said Major Southall sharply. 'What is it that we want to know, eh?'

John flushed and looked in anguish at Father Huddleston, who came forward and put a hand on his shoulder.

'All you have to do, John, my boy,' he said kindly, 'is to answer the questions Major Southall asks you. Answer him simply and truthfully – as far as your conscience and your duty permit.'

Father Huddleston squeezed John's shoulder slightly.

'Please leave the boy alone,' said the major, 'and do not incite him to falsehood.'

'I only bade him to be truthful,' said Father Huddleston. 'You would not have him speak against his conscience and sense of duty, surely? Is not the liberty of the subject one of the main ideals of your new form of Government?'

'I will not bandy words with you, sir! Kindly hold your tongue and allow me to conduct this affair in my own way.'

'But, of course,' said Father Huddleston blandly. 'I would not interfere for the world.'

The major glared at Father Huddleston and then turned to the secretary. 'Read the proclamation to this boy,' he said.

'Yes, sir,' said the secretary. He picked up a piece of paper and read it. 'Be it known that, by order of the Council of the Parliament of England, it is hereby proclaimed that any person who hides, or who helps to hide the rebel, Charles Stuart, or who having certain information of his whereabouts wilfully withholds it from the authorities, shall be deemed guilty of High Treason, and on conviction shall be hanged.'

'Do you understand that?' the major asked John.

'Yes, sir. Is there not also a reward of a thousand pounds for him who betrays the King.'

'The King, forsooth!' said the major. 'We have no King in England, nor ever shall again! It is the rebel, Charles Stuart, son of the late King, we seek.'

'Yes, sir,' said John, and again rebuked himself for being cheeky when there was no need.

'However, let us get on. You have lived here for several months, I believe?' He had suddenly become friendly and casual.

'Yes, sir, about seven months.'

'Then you know the house well? You and the other two boys must have great times exploring this rambling mansion.'

'Oh yes, sir,' said John, relieved at the turn things had taken. 'We play hide-and-seek and other games.'

'I used to play hide-and-seek when I was a boy,' said the major, 'but I never had such a splendid house as this for my games. I expect there are some good hiding places, eh?'

'Oh yes, sir,' said John. He was going to enlarge on the subject when he noticed that the other two officers had leaned forward to listen carefully, the secretary had dipped a new pen in the ink, and Father Huddleston was suddenly afflicted with a troublesome cough. John flushed at his simplicity.

'Go on, Sir John, tell us about your games of hide-and-seek,' said the officer on the major's left.

'They are very good, sir, as the house is large. We hide under beds and in cupboards and I have a special place.'

'Yes? Where is that?' the major asked.

'Inside the seat of the chair you are using, sir. The seat is a large box, and I can just get inside.'

The three officers stared at him hard and then relaxed. John thought, 'That was a close one, but I needn't have invented the hiding place.'

For a few moments there was silence in the room. John looked at the three officers, and saw that they were all staring at him. He looked down at his feet and waited. He had an absurd desire to say something, anything rather than to have to stand there being stared at.

'Have you seen the man who is hiding in this house?' the major suddenly asked.

John's brain raced and he clenched his fists.

'What man, sir?' he said.

'There is a man, a Royalist fugitive from Worcester fight hiding in this house. Have you seen him?'

'Who is it, sir?'

'Don't be impertinent, boy,' snapped the major, suddenly harsh.

'If anyone was hidden here,' said Father Huddleston in his mild and reasonable voice, 'the boys would not be told about it.'

'Hold your tongue!' the major snapped. 'You, boy, look at me. Have you seen Charles Stuart?'

'Charles Stuart, sir?' said John, in a misery of anxiety.

'Answer me!' roared the major, thumping the table with his fist. 'Have you seen Charles Stuart?'

'I don't know, sir,' said John. Then he realized that it was the wrong thing to say. He knew that 'I don't know' always angers grown-ups.

'Answer me yes or no! Have you seen Charles Stuart?'

'I don't know if I have or not, sir,' said John, with a splendid look of innocence. 'I don't know what he looks like, and we have seen so many people these past few days.'

'Oh! what people, where?'

'Oh, soldiers, sir, searching the house, and marching up and down the road, and friends of Mr Whitgreave come for news of the battle, and Scottish soldiers, sir, walking northwards.'

'Pah, you are trifling with me, boy! Listen, we have reason to believe that Charles Stuart is hiding in some big house in these parts. We know one or more rebels have been hidden in this house. Now, have you seen Charles Stuart in this house?'

The major had become red in the face and the fact that he was angry gave John courage; he put on the helpful and dutiful expression which had often helped him with grown-ups.

'I'm sorry, sir, but as I said, I don't know. I can't say I haven't seen the King – I mean – Charles Stuart, because I wouldn't know if I did.'

The bored-looking officer suddenly pointed a finger at John. 'This house is being searched by men skilled in the art. If anyone is hiding here he will be discovered. If it is the rebel, Charles Stuart, then you will be adjudged guilty of withholding information and that is High Treason!'

'I protest,' said Father Huddleston, 'you will confuse the boy.'

'Be quiet!' said the major. 'Well, boy, what have you to say?'

John began to feel panic.

'I don't know what the question is, sir,' he said.

'Well, answer this. Have you seen any stranger in this house today?'

John wanted to deny it at once, but something in his mind warned him to be careful. A direct lie could lead to trouble.

'I have told you, sir, we have seen a great many people, coming and going.'

The officer on Southall's right leaned over and said something in a low voice. The other said something as well, and Southall nodded. 'Yes,' he said, 'that should do the trick.' He

D

looked across at the soldier at the door. 'Fetch the boy we had first, Tom Palyn.'

'Yes, sir,' said the soldier, and went out.

'Your friend told us a different tale, as you shall hear. Perhaps this will make you tell us what you know,' Southall said to John.

There was silence in the room while they waited. John tried to think clearly. He knew they were going to try to catch him out against something Tom had said. But his mind was confused and he could only count the panes of glass in the great window. Father Huddleston cleared his throat to speak but Southall silenced him with a curt, 'Hold your tongue, you!'

They all watched Tom as he came in with the soldier. Tom was pale but he gave a little smile to John. He went to John's side and took his hand, and together they faced Major Southall.

'Now, Master Tom Palyn,' he said, 'you told us that you have seen no strangers at all in this house today.'

Tom glanced at John and then looked straight at Southall.

'That's right, sir.'

Southall looked at John. 'You hear that?' he said. 'You say you've seen a great many. Well?'

John's mind was in a whirl, he didn't know how to answer. But there was no need, for at that moment the door was opened quickly and another officer hurried in.

'We've found him, sir!' he said.

The three officers and the secretary sprang to their feet. Father Huddleston put his hands to his face. John and Tom turned towards the door.

'Where?' said Southall.

'In a cunningly contrived hiding place, sir. We tapped and found a false door. Shall I bring him in?'

'Yes, at once,' said Major Southall.

John and Tom went over to Father Huddleston, and he put a hand on each boy's shoulder. John thought, 'I can't bear to see him a prisoner!'

There was the noise of heavy boots on the oak floor and two soldiers came in, each firmly grasping an arm of – Mr Whitgreave.

'Oh, God be praised,' muttered Father Huddleston, and he tightened his grip on the boys. 'Show no surprise,' he whispered.

'Who the devil are you?' the major asked.

'By the same token, who the devil are you!' said Mr Whitgreave. 'I am Thomas Whitgreave, owner of this house. Kindly tell your ruffians to release my arms.'

The major sat down. 'We hoped you were someone else,' he said. 'All right, let him go. Now, Mr Whitgreave, why were you in a secret hiding place?'

'Because I saw you come and wish to have as little to do with you as possible.'

'You bore arms against us in the rebellion, I believe?'

'I did. I commanded a troop in Lord Wilmot's regiment of Horse, for which I have been fined ten thousand pounds.'

'You also fought for the rebel, Charles Stuart, at Worcester?'

'I did not. I was ill and kept the house, as a score of witnesses will testify.'

Father Huddleston quietly led the boys from the room. Everyone was so occupied with Mr Whitgreave that they took no notice. Outside Father Huddleston said, 'Bravely done, John. Your father would have been proud of you.'

At that John suddenly found his eyes fill with tears. He wanted to be alone.

An hour later the three boys watched Major Southall and the others ride away, followed by a squadron of horse. They did a war dance, slapped each other on the back, and made wild hunting noises. They were in the middle of this noisy celebration when Father Huddleston came to the door. He grinned at them.

'You are wanted in the drawing-room,' he said, 'and brush your hair and tidy yourselves up.'

They knocked at the drawing-room door and went in, as demure a trio of boys as could be desired. Mr Whitgreave was standing by the window with Father Huddleston.

'Come in, you three,' said Mr Whitgreave. 'Father Huddleston has told me how bravely you faced the ordeal in this room.'

'Uncle,' said Tom, 'they didn't arrest you then?'

'No. It was all part of a plan. I knew they wouldn't be happy until they had a victim, so I hid behind a secret panel and when they came near I made sure that they would hear me. I sneezed.'

'But, sir,' said John, 'they were very angry with you.'

'Yes, weren't they! But I was able to prove I was not at Worcester fight, so all ended well. Now, boys, I have decided to reward your constancy. You knew I had an important guest here, you knew he was in hiding, and when you were questioned not one of you faltered. So, come with me.'

They followed him out of the door and along the corridor into a small room Mr Whitgreave used as his study. Sitting at a table sipping a glass of wine was Mr Will Jones.

'Sir,' said Mr Whitgreave, making a bow, 'these are the three boys I told you about. These two, Tom Palyn and Frank Reynolds, are my nephews. This other – Sir John Preston – is the son of an old friend.'

Will Jones looked at each boy in turn and nodded to him in a friendly way. When he looked at John he gave him the slightest of winks, as between confederates.

'Boys,' said Mr Whitgreave, 'this is a great moment in your lives. This is my master, your master, the master of us all. His Majesty the King!'

The boys bowed low.

'And very happy I am to meet you, my young friends,' said the King, 'for I have heard how well you have served me this day. You have been my Lifeguards, and right stoutly did you protect me.'

He held out his right hand and the boys went up in turn, dropped on one knee, and kissed it. As John knelt Mr Whitgreave said, 'It was a blessing, Your Majesty, that they did not know that you were here. So heavy a secret would have been more than young heads could have borne.'

'Oh, I don't know,' said the King. 'What say you, Sir John?'

John looked at the King and smiled at him.

'Oh, I don't know, Your Majesty,' he said.

CHAPTER EIGHT

JANE LANE'S NEW SERVANT

THE King arrived at Bentley Hall about midnight on 9th
September. Lord Wilmot had ridden to Moseley Hall and
had conducted him to Colonel Lane's mansion, about mid-
way between Willenhall and Walsall, twenty miles north-
west of the little town of Birmingham. Colonel Lane was
waiting at the gate to welcome the King, and led him into the
house.

In the parlour Colonel Lane lighted more candles, Lord

Wilmot stirred the fire with his boot, and the King sat down and looked about him.

'So ends another day,' he said, 'the sixth since I have been on the run. Zounds, I have been at liberty for nearly a week!'

'This day seems to have been the most perilous of them all, Sire,' said Lord Wilmot.

'Aye, Henry, I felt uncommonly like a trapped animal, lying low in my hiding place. I heard them open the door of the cupboard above my head, but by good fortune they didn't notice the trap-door. And if three lads hadn't kept their heads I'd have lost mine. Whitgreave saved the day, by getting himself discovered. They were so glad to have one victim that they gave up their suspicion that I might be there. I imagine General Harrison is becoming vexed at his failure to catch me!'

'Long may he remain vexed,' said Colonel Lane. 'A glass of wine and some biscuits, Sire?'

'Thank you, Colonel. Your very good health!'

'And good fortune, Your Majesty,' said Lane.

'And a malediction on Oliver!' said Lord Wilmot.

When they had put down their glasses the King said, 'Well, what plans have you hatched up for me?'

'There is an idea of getting you to Bristol, Sire,' said Wilmot, 'but I have another which is nearer my heart. It will mean an end to hole-and-corner business, to disguises and subterfuge.'

'What is that, Henry?'

'To go to the woods, sir, you and I and such good fellows as the Penderels. There to collect others of like mind, true men who love their King. Our band would grow rapidly. We could strike back at the Roundheads instead of running away from them, and by my heart, sir, I dearly want to strike back!'

'A kind of a Robin Hood existence, eh?' said the King.

'Yes, sir, but with an even better cause. We would work in secret, move swiftly from one place to another, use the great houses of your friends as headquarters when necessary. We could raid the enemy, set him in confusion, and, sir, you would soon find yourself at the head of an army of valiant men.

Then, we would work towards London. We could get the apprentices to rise, and the men of spirit in London who are growing weary of the preaching and solemnity.'

Lord Wilmot had paced up and down as he spoke, his eyes alight with enthusiasm, the fighting man spoiling for a fight. He turned appealingly to the King.

'Henry, my friend,' said the King, 'how like you! For the moment I was almost won over. But it cannot be. Enough good men have been slain for me, I want no more of war and strife. If God wills that I am preserved and come back to reign I shall be no warrior king. I shall foster the arts of peace, not of war. A stout navy to guard our shores we must have. Behind that shield, I would encourage scientific discovery and good living. I would have my people cheerful and busy, not soldiers and sailors – and widows and orphans. But I run ahead. First I must save my skin. And, Henry, I need your valiant heart to guard me, there will be dangers enough, I warrant you, so be content with protecting your fugitive King.'

'Have no fear about that, Sire,' said Wilmot. 'It was – just a dream.'

'I live on dreams these days, Henry,' the King said, taking his hand. 'Now, what is this talk of Bristol?' he asked briskly.

'I have a pass, Your Majesty,' said Colonel Lane, 'to permit my sister Jane, her servant, and her kinsman, Cornet Henry Lassells, to travel to Bristol. It is signed by the Governor of Stafford. Here it is, Your Majesty,' said the colonel, taking a folded document from a drawer in a desk. 'You, Sire, could be the servant.'

'Very neat, very neat indeed,' said the King.

'Henry Lassells will go with you as escort,' went on the colonel, 'and Lord Wilmot and I will follow at a safe distance.'

'What think you of the design, Sire?' Wilmot asked.

'I think it excellent, Henry, in every way. I would rather ride bold by daylight than skulk about at night. And above all I shall be moving towards a definite goal. Yes, it is excellent.'

'I have prepared some suitable clothes, Your Majesty,' said

Colonel Lane. 'Two good linen shirts of my own and this suit and cloak of plain grey cloth, such as a farmer's son might wear. I hope that these boots will fit better than the ones you are wearing. I have put twenty pounds in the pocket for the journey.'

'This is wonderful,' said the King, 'clean linen and a good suit, and boots which will not pinch my toes and rub my heels raw. Perhaps I can have my hair trimmed; this country cut of the good Penderels may look the part of a woodman, but I am vain enough to prefer not to look like a last-season's scarecrow. When may I meet your sister, Colonel?'

'Jane is waiting, Sire, in case you should wish to see her, and Henry Lassells too.'

'Then let us meet.'

Colonel Lane went off and the King fingered the linen shirt appreciatively.

'Henry,' he said suddenly, 'I feel more hopeful than ever before. If we can find a loyal ship's master at Bristol, we shall be safe in France within the week.'

'God willing, sir!'

Colonel Lane came back with his sister, a pretty young lady with a vivacious manner and a quick smile. She curtsied low, while young Henry Lassells bowed and stood nervously just inside the door. The King went across to Miss Lane and held out his hand, which she kissed.

'Your servant, Mistress,' he said, 'and I do not use the word in the formal manner. I am charmed that I am indeed to be your servant and I trust you will find me a suitable one and attentive.'

'The honour is mine, Your Majesty,' she said, 'and I hope that my company will not weary you.'

'Ha, I am never wearied of the company of a pretty lady, Mistress. Zounds, I begin to enjoy my adventures.' He turned to Henry Lassells and gave him his hand to kiss. 'Well met, Cornet Lassells,' he said, 'I am sure we shall be safe with you as our escort.'

'The honour is too much, Your Majesty,' said Lassells. 'I am – at a loss for words. I never dreamed that I should have such a charge laid on me. I will die, Sire, in your service.'

'I sincerely hope you won't!' said the King. He turned to Colonel Lane. 'At what hour do we leave tomorrow?'

'When it suits Your Majesty. We thought about eight o'clock?'

'Eight o'clock it shall be. And we should muster in some quiet spot before that so that you can teach me the proper manners for a servant, and show me what I must do and what I must not do.'

'Your Majesty does not expect me to treat you really as a servant!' said Miss Lane.

'Oh, but you must,' said Lord Wilmot. 'There will be sharp eyes about you. One blunder and all will be lost. Besides, your sister and her husband, the Peters, are riding with you part of the way and they do not know our secret. You must always address His Majesty as Will Jones.'

'No, not Will Jones,' said the King, 'I am heartily sick of that fellow. He was an ill-clad fellow, as you can see, Mistress; unkempt, and usually soaked to the skin. He limped and he led an owl's life, sleeping by day and fluttering about in the shadows by night. No, I'll have no more of Will Jones. Let me be someone else. I know, Will Jackson, a new name for a new person.' The King bowed low to Mistress Lane. 'Will Jackson, Mistress, at your service. Yours to command, and remember to cuff my ears if I do wrong.'

'Oh, but I cannot,' she said.

'But you must,' said the King. 'Come, call me by my name.' Jane hesitated, and then smiled at the fun of it.

'Will!' she said imperiously, pointing to her shoe, 'my lace is undone. Fasten it.'

'At once, Mistress,' said the King, going to her and kneeling.

'No, Sire, no!' cried Henry Lassells in anguish, rushing forward.

The King looked up at him. 'Cornet Lassells, you forget

yourself! I am Will Jackson, your kinswoman's servant. Kindly treat me as such.'

Lassells looked embarrassed.

'Come on, what is my name?' the King said.

'Will – Will Jackson, Your Majesty,' said Lassells.

'No! *Not* "Your Majesty",' said the King. 'Do you want to have me captured and led before Noll Cromwell?'

'I am sorry, Sire – Will,' said Lassells.

The King fastened Jane's shoe-lace and got up. They all laughed.

'Now to bed,' said the King, 'and tomorrow we will rehearse our parts, and 'faith it seems I am not the only one with much to learn.'

At eight o'clock the next morning Colonel Lane's mother stood on the steps in front of Bentley Hall to watch her daughter, Jane, set off on her journey to Bristol. Jane's elder sister, Withy, and her husband, Mr Peters, were also there to ride with Jane as far as Stratford-on-Avon. Cornet Lassells and Lord Wilmot were watching Jane's new servant talking to his mistress.

It was a bright morning of warm sun and there was an air of holiday about the gathering. Colonel Lane's mother noticed that her son and Lord Wilmot were in excellent spirits, but young Henry Lassells seemed to have something on his mind. She went down the steps to join them. As she approached she heard her daughter say to the servant who was holding her horse, 'His name's Yorick, he's very sweet. I love him.'

'He'll need to be strong, too, to carry both you and me,' the servant replied, 'but I like the look of him, he's worthy of being a royal charger.'

'See if his bit is easy, Will,' Jane said, suddenly brusque, for she had seen her mother approaching.

'Very good, Mistress,' said the servant.

'Ah, Jane, my dear, I wanted to make sure you had got the pass to take you to Bristol,' said her mother.

'Yes, Will has it, Mother. You have got the pass, Will, haven't you?'

'Yes, Mistress,' said Will.

'Who is that new servant, Jane?' her mother said, looking at him. Lord Wilmot had come up and he answered.

'He is a servant of mine, Ma'am, and a very good man. As the journey is somewhat hazardous I have lent him to Miss Jane.'

'I see. That's very kind of you, my lord. He seemed to me to have rather a saucy, confident way with him.'

'Oh, Will's a much travelled servant,' said Lord Wilmot. 'He means no harm, I assure you.'

'I see. Well, my man,' she said to Will, 'take good care of your mistress, remember your place, and don't go drinking with the other servants or fighting. We want no trouble.'

'I'll do my duty, Ma'am,' said Will, 'and remember my place. Are we ready to go, my lord?' he asked.

'Yes, Will, you can mount.'

Mrs Lane went back a few yards and the servant leapt nimbly into the saddle in front of Mistress Jane. They were both riding Yorick, and the strawberry roan shuffled on his feet at the double weight. Lord Wilmot was holding his head, and he took the opportunity to speak quietly to the servant.

'Have a care, Sire, remember to be respectful and demure. The Peters don't know who you are and poor young Henry Lassells just can't get used to treating you as a servant!'

'I'll do my best, Henry, and I think I'm going to enjoy myself!'

'Come, Will, you knave,' said Jane sharply, 'I am ready, and so is everyone else.'

'Very good, Mistress,' said Will, and Lord Wilmot stood aside.

'Be very careful, all of you,' said Mrs Lane. 'Do not annoy any soldiers you may have to deal with. These are dangerous days, and there are desperate men abroad, as well as the troops!'

With a general chorus of farewells the cavalcade set off. Cornet Lassells led, Mr and Mrs Peters went next, and Jane Lane and her servant, on the strawberry roan, followed them. Mrs Lane watched them anxiously as they turned into the high road and broke into a trot.

'I do hope they will be all right,' she said to Lord Wilmot. 'I don't like my two daughters riding so far in these troubled times. I must say, your servant looks a very unusual kind of man, Lord Wilmot!'

'Oh, he is, Ma'am, Will Jackson's most unusual,' said Lord Wilmot. 'I think the world of him.'

The little party riding along the dusty roads aroused no particular comment. In two hours they reached the village of Bromsgrove, and there Jane's horse cast a shoe. They stopped at a forge, and dismounted to take refreshment at the inn across the road while the horse was shod.

'I'll see to the horse,' said Lassells.

'Oh no, you won't, Henry,' said Jane. 'My servant will do that.' She turned to the servant. 'See the blacksmith does the job properly, Will, and don't stand gossiping with him.'

'Very good, Mistress,' said Will, and he led the horse into the smithy. The others went into the inn, though Lassells seemed loath to leave Jane's horse and her servant.

Will Jackson leaned against the wall watching the smith at work.

'Come far, friend?' the smith asked.

'About two hours' ride from the north. I'm going to Bristol with my mistress.'

'Nice horse this, though the smith who shod him last didn't know his job very well. We'll soon put that right for you, old fellow.' He went to the furnace and held the new shoe in the flames with long tongs, while his boy pumped the bellows.

'Have you heard any news of late?' Will said.

'Nothing much. Cromwell routed the Scots at Worcester good and proper last week, which is a great mercy.'

'Yes,' said Will Jackson.

'Most of them were slain,' went on the smith, examining the red-hot horse-shoe and spitting on it, 'and the rest who escaped have mostly been took. But they say Charles Stuart escaped.'

'I expect he made his way by back ways to Scotland,' said Will Jackson.

'That's not very likely. Whoa, lad, let's have that hoof.' He lifted the hoof and with his tongs laid the red hot shoe on it. Expertly he held the horse's hoof on his knees against his leather apron and put the nails in his mouth. One by one he drove them in. When the shoe was firmly nailed on he said, 'If you ask me Charles Stuart is lurking secretly somewhere in England, in these parts I shouldn't wonder. I wish I knew where he was.'

'Why, what would you do?'

'What would I do?' said the smith, watching carefully as the horse put its hoof to the ground, 'why, I'd knock him on the head, and carry him to the soldiers, and get a thousand pounds reward. Wouldn't you?'

'Yes, of course,' said Will Jackson. 'A thousand pounds is a lot of money.'

'I'll agree with you there, friend. That will be sixpence, and it's as well shod a hoof as you'll get in this Commonwealth of England.'

The journey was uneventful for the next two hours, as they rode across country towards Stratford-on-Avon. Then, near the village of Bearley, they came across a troop of cavalry resting by the roadside. Lassells reined in his horse and they formed a group round him.

'What do we do now?' said Lassells.

'We'd better take to the fields and make a detour to Stratford-on-Avon,' said Peters.

'Why not go on? We've got a pass,' said Jane.

'If we do take to the fields they might see us,' said Will Jackson, 'and get suspicious. It would be better to ride down the road quite naturally.'

'If you think that is best, Sir – I mean Will,' said Lassells, just managing to choke back the word Sire.

'No,' said Peters. 'We'll go across country and avoid them.'

'Will here says it's better to keep to the road,' said Lassells.

'I don't care a straw what Will says,' said Peters. 'I don't take my orders from servants. And it will be better if you don't interfere, my man, when your betters are talking!'

'I beg your pardon, sir,' said Will demurely, 'but if they are riding to Stratford as well, and if we take to the fields, we may well come across them again.'

'I will not be argued with by a servant!' said Peters. 'Kindly hold your tongue!'

Lassell's eyes had opened wide with horror at this, and Jane exploded suddenly with mirth, and then covered it by pretending she had swallowed a fly.

They rode on, leaving the road and making a wide detour. They had to join the road again, because the river Avon can only be crossed by the bridge in the town, and in the outskirts of the town they came upon the soldiers again, halted in the road.

'There you are,' said Jane. 'Will was right. Now we will have to ride through them.'

'Excuse me, sir,' said Will, 'permit me to go first, to clear the way.'

He shook the reins and the horse quickened its pace. The soldiers were standing all over the road.

'Make way there!' Will called out, 'make way for travellers!'

The soldiers looked round and moved their horses to make a clear passage down the middle of the road.

'Good day to you, friends,' said Will cheerfully, touching his hat. The others followed suit.

''Day to you, friend,' said the soldiers. Some of them raised their hands in salute.

'A fine day, Sergeant,' said Will as he came up with him.

'Somewhat too hot for my liking, friend,' said the sergeant, and he nodded his head to Miss Jane, Mr and Mrs Peters, and Lassells.

They rode into Stratford-on-Avon, paused to say good-bye to the Peters, and then approached the bridge over the Avon. Lassells wanted to break into a gallop, but Will Jackson stopped him.

'Ride in a leisurely manner, and look at ease,' he said.

After a mile or two they turned right along a by-road to Long Marston, where they were to spend the first night at the house of Mr Tomes, a relative of the Lanes. He was expecting his visitors, and came out when he heard their horses and helped Jane to dismount.

'This is splendid, my dear,' he said, 'I was anxious in case the soldiers should stop you. Now, come inside, and you, Henry. Your servant can help my groom tend the horses. Jack,' he said to his groom, who had come running out, 'see that Miss Jane's servant is made comfortable in the servants' quarters, and well looked after in the kitchen. Come, my dear.'

He put an arm round Jane's waist and led her off. Lassells hesitated, looking at Will Jackson.

'I shall be quite all right, thank you, sir,' said Will politely, but he scowled fiercely at Lassells and signed for him to go.

As he led Yorick towards the loose-boxes, the groom led Lassell's horse, and said:

'Have a good journey, friend?'

'Very good, thank you.'

'What's your name?'

'Me? I'm Will, Will Jackson. What's yours?'

'I'm Jack. Put him in there. You groom the strawberry roan and I'll see to this one. I expect you're hungry.'

'Yes, and thirsty too,' said Will.

'Oh, we'll soon set a pot of ale before you. Look lively, man!'

CHAPTER NINE

WILL JACKSON IN THE KITCHEN

WHEN the horses were settled into their loose-boxes Jack led
Will Jackson to the kitchen.

'You'd best beware of Bridget,' he said, 'speak her fair and
never dispute with her, or she can be a tartar, a regular tartar.'

'Who's Bridget?'

'Bridget's the cook, and a wonderful cook she is, as you'll
find. But she's queen of her kitchen is Bridget, and she keeps
us all in our place. So don't say much and do what she tells you
sharp, see?'

Jack opened the door and Will Jackson followed him in. But in the doorway they stopped, for a fat woman was beating a cowering man with a large frying pan. As she shouted at him she banged him with the pan, on the shoulders, on his head, which he was trying to protect with his hands, on the back, everywhere.

'You great ignorant simpleton,' she shouted, 'whipping cream in the dish that's just been used for making soap! What kind of a sillabub will that be for the master's table! How can I watch everything, with supper for two extra, and all to be special! You dundering great nincompoop you.'

'I washed it, Mistress Bridget, I washed it proper first.'

'Answer me back, would you! Take that! Now go and sharpen that knife on the table, and be quick about it.'

'Yes, Mistress Bridget, Ma'am,' said the man. He seized the knife and hurried to the door. Jack timidly advanced into the room, and Will Jackson with him.

'So there you are, Jack! And about time too. Who's that good-for-nothing you've brought with you?'

'Please, Bridget,' said Jack, 'it's Will Jackson, Mistress Lane's servant. Master says you were to look after him in the kitchen!'

Will Jackson smiled as nicely as he could, but it was only a rather nervous smile. Bridget put her hands on her hips.

'Oh, indeed!' she said, 'as though I've not enough to do as it is without looking after other people's servants! Custards to make, rabbits to stew, a joint to roast and now I'm to play the hostess to *you*. Well, you can make yourself useful. Go tend the roasting-spit.'

'Gladly, Mistress, gladly,' said Will Jackson, hurrying across the kitchen to the roaring fire.

'And you, Jack, wash your hands of the stable-smell and skin those rabbits. Prudence, you whip the cream,' she said, to a pretty kitchen wench who was gazing with interest at the handsome newcomer. Will Jackson smiled at her in a friendly way, caught Bridget's eye, and turned his attention to the joint on the spit. He picked up the heavy spoon, dipped it in a bowl of fat, and basted the joint. He felt he should do something else but couldn't think what it was. He was concentrating on his task when he suddenly received a resounding slap on the side of his face. He jumped up to see Bridget standing in front of him.

'You great fool you,' she said, 'you'll ruin the joint! Turn it, man, turn it.'

'Your pardon, Mistress, but – how?'

'How? You say how? You, in service to gentlefolk and you don't know how to use a roasting-jack? Where were you brought up, eh?'

'I am sorry, Ma'am, I'm only an outside servant, you see. And my home was so poor we never had much in the way of meat to eat.'

'Hm. A sorry fellow you are! Pru, come you here, show this stupid how to roast meat.'

'Yes'm,' said Prudence, hurrying across.

When Prudence had shown Will how to operate the roasting-jack, kneeling by his side in front of the hot fire, she looked at him kindly.

'Where d'you live?' she said.

'Oh, with my master and mistress.'

'I mean, where's your home, your own home.'

'Oh, I haven't got one now. I don't live anywhere.'

'Oh, poor Will,' she said, putting her hand on his.

The door opened and Will turned to see who it was, and jumped up. It was a trooper of Militia, in uniform.

'Hello, Aunt Bridget,' he said.

'Why, Mike, my dear, welcome! Come you in. You, Will, go to the cellar and bring a quart of ale, the best, from the big barrel in the corner. You, Pru, cut a tasty slice off that joint. Luke, fetch some of the new baked bread. Why, Mike, let me look at you!' she said, kissing the soldier and hugging him.

The soldier sat down and took off his helmet, and Will

Jackson, seeing that he took no notice of him, went down the stairs in the corner to the cellar, filled a quart pot with beer, drank half of it, filled it again, and took it up to the kitchen.

'Your beer, friend,' he said as he put it on the table.

'Thank you, my man,' said the soldier.

When the soldier was settled with newly roasted meat, newly baked bread, and the best beer, everyone returned to their duties.

'Mistress Bridget fair dotes on that oaf of a nephew of hers,' Prudence whispered to Will as they sat by the roasting joint. 'Why did you jump up when he came in?'

'Did I?'

'Of course you did, and you looked proper startled too!'

'Oh, soldiers mean trouble these days,' said Will, 'but look, the joint wants turning.'

Soon afterwards Mr Tomes came into the kitchen with Cornet Lassells, and all the servants stood up respectfully; even the trooper rose to his feet.

'Ah, sorry to disturb you, Bridget,' said Mr Tomes. 'Mistress Lane wanted to know if her manservant was all right.'

'He's well enough, Master,' said Bridget, 'though I had to box his ears to teach him how to work the roasting-jack.'

A look of horror came to Lassells' face. He looked across at Will Jackson, but Will winked cheerfully at him. Lassells also looked suspiciously at the soldier.

'Ah,' said Mr Tomes to Will, 'my Bridget is a martinet in her kitchen, but she's the best cook in the land. Glad to see your nephew is here, Bridget, even if he is a Parliament soldier. Will supper be ready soon?'

'Very shortly now, sir.'

'Good. Come, Henry.' With a benevolent smile at all in the room Mr Tomes turned and went. Lassells stood uncertainly for a moment, looking anxiously at Will and the soldier, and then he went out as well.

When the supper was taken through to the dining-room and

the dishes were cleared away the servants sat down at the table for their supper. Bridget sat at the head of the table with her nephew next to her, quite ready for a second supper, and Will Jackson sat next to him. Prudence sat opposite to Will, and she obviously felt friendly disposed towards him. It was an excellent supper, and as Bridget was in a good mood because her military nephew had come, it was all very pleasant.

'Well, have they caught the King yet?' Luke said after a while.

'Not yet,' said the soldier, 'but it won't be long now. They know where he is I'm told.'

'Oh, the poor young man,' said Bridget.

'It's a shame, the way they've hunted him and hounded him,' said Prudence.

'And they'll go and chop his head off, like they did his father's,' said Jack.

'As I'm off duty,' said the soldier, 'and among friends, I don't mind saying that I agree with you. I hope he'll escape. It's not his fault he was unlucky in his birth. What say you, Will Jackson?'

'The Government have declared him an enemy,' said Will Jackson, 'and he brought an army into England.'

'Wouldn't you have done the same,' said Bridget, 'if you'd been the Prince of Wales, and your father, anointed and true born King of the realm, martyred? Wouldn't you have tried to win your crown back? Of course you would!'

'Well, I can't tell, not being the King,' said Will.

'It's funny you should say that,' said the soldier, looking at Will, 'because it so happens that you are very like him.'

'Coo,' said Prudence, 'is the King tall and handsome, then, like Mr Jackson?' Then she blushed.

'Have you seen him, Mike?' said Luke.

'Of course he has,' said Bridget with pride, 'haven't you, Mike?'

'Oh yes, many times,' said Mike. 'I saw him at Worcester. He fought like a proper man, he did.' He turned his chair the better to study Will Jackson. 'He's the same colouring as Will here, and he's got the same look about him. But the King's taller, holds himself better, and he's broader. Will here's what you might call a poor imitation of the King.'

'He must be wonderful,' said Prudence with a sigh.

'Well, I'm glad I'm only Will Jackson,' said Will, 'and not Charles Stuart.'

'"Charles Stuart" indeed,' said Bridget sharply, 'none of that here. We give the poor young man his proper title in *this* kitchen! The young man is the eldest son of the poor martyred King, and heir of kings and queens for a thousand years and more, and for all the pompous old stuck-up Puritan pigs say in Parliament, he's the King of England, poor young man!' She glared angrily at Will Jackson, and he found that everyone else round the table was doing the same, except Prudence, who was looking hurt.

'I only used the name he's called according to the law of the land,' he said.

'If you start belittling His Majesty,' said Luke, 'I'll take you outside and give you a dusting. Answer me direct. If you discovered him, would you give him up?'

Will hesitated for a moment. 'Yes,' he said, 'I would, for it would be my duty to do so. And a thousand pounds is a deal of money for a poor man.'

'Then you're a scoundrel,' said Luke, 'a cowardly, greedy scoundrel!'

'We don't want none of that talk here,' said Jack, more moderately.

Bridget's nephew finished off his second plate of apple-pie and cleared his throat. 'It's my duty to apprehend all rebels, as they call them,' he said, 'me being in the Militia, into which I was enlisted against my will without being asked. It would be my duty to apprehend His Majesty if I had the chance, but I'd be mortal sorry so to do.'

'There's a good boy,' said Bridget, 'have another plateful of this tart.'

'Are all your comrades in the Militia of a like mind?' Will Jackson asked.

'Oh, I wouldn't say that,' said the soldier. 'Most of us does our duty because that's what's right. There are some who feel strongly about it. They'd cut his throat and sing a psalm as they did it. Then there's another kind, mostly the officers and sergeants. They're as full of high-sounding reasons as a pudding is of plums, and talk of the good of the state, and freedom, and the beauties of Government by Parliament. They're the dangerous ones. Mark you, some of them at the top are only thinking of themselves and the high office they can get.'

'It was downright wicked,' said Bridget, 'to cut off the head of the King, the Lord's anointed.'

'He wasn't a bad king,' said Luke.

'He was a good man,' said Bridget, 'and a good husband and father. Don't you agree, Mr Jackson?'

'Certainly, Mistress,' said Will, 'it seems he was a very good father to his children.'

'Poor things,' said Bridget, 'all living in exile in France where they eat frogs and I don't know what and don't have no wholesome puddings. And the rightful King, hunted and hounded in his own realm, and lurking I don't know where, and in I don't know what manner of company.'

'And you,' said Luke, pointing at Will Jackson, 'you'd give him up to be murdered!'

'I'm sure you wouldn't really,' said Prudence, looking at Will with her eyes bright, 'you're much too nice and good. And how I would love to see the King, just to see him! He's only twenty-one and taller even than Mr Jackson, and even more handsome. Oh,' she said dreamily, 'I'd swoon if I saw him!'

'Don't sit there looking all moony,' said Luke, 'you're always dreaming of other men. I suppose you imagine being kissed by the King!'

'You've no right to speak to me like that, Luke Tomkins,'

Prudence said sharply, 'I'm not promised to you, for all you think!'

'Luke'll have you, Pru,' said Jack, 'and you know it!'

'Not if he tries to order me about he won't,' said Prudence. Then she put her chin in her hands and said dreamily, 'To be kissed by King Charles! Oh, I'd be happy for the rest of my days!'

'Stuff and nonsense,' said Bridget. 'Mike, my dear, have some of this cheese, it's the Master's special one, with his best Madeira wine poured into it.'

Later that night Will Jackson went into the garden. It was a soft, warm night, and there was a strong scent of roses among the trimly cut hedges. He leaned against the trunk of an apple-tree and listened, and his thoughts slipped away to summer evenings long ago in the gardens of Richmond Palace.

Then there had been soft music from the Court musicians, men and women in splendid clothes of silk and satin, and his father, grave and affectionate. He thought of his mother, always exquisitely dressed, vivacious, and talking with French words mixed with the English. He thought of his brothers and sisters, clever Mary, and little Henrietta, his favourite, and James, who was so serious, and young Henry, who was always getting into scrapes. He sighed, full of memories of happy days now past.

His reverie was broken by a furtive sound in the shadows behind him. Instantly on guard, he swung round and saw – Prudence.

'Hello, Mr Jackson,' she said.

'Hello, Prudence. What a lovely night.'

'Yes,' she said and went close to him. He slipped his arm round her waist.

'Mistress Bridget's nephew said I was very like the King,' he said. 'If you shut your eyes, you could imagine I was King Charles.'

'Yes, I suppose I could,' she said. There was a little pause and then she said, very coyly, 'I've got my eyes shut.'

'And I'm the King of England,' said Will Jackson, and he kissed her. 'There, kissed by the King of England!'

'Oh, you are nice,' she said, 'and I've still got them shut.'

As Will kissed her again he was suddenly seized and pulled away. Prudence gave a little scream and Will clenched his fists.

It was Luke. 'You blackguard!' he said. 'Pru's my girl. Put your fists up, I'm going to give you a thorough dusting!'

'Luke, don't!' said Prudence, hanging on to him. But he shook her off, and went closer to Will and slapped his face.

'Now put your fists up,' he said. 'You come here, talk like a stuck-up Puritan Roundhead, and then you try to steal my girl.

'I am sorry,' said Will Jackson. 'I kissed her against her will. It won't happen again.'

'I'll see it doesn't,' said Luke. 'Put your fists up.'

Will put his fists up and they squared up to each other, while Prudence stood by with her hands to her mouth. But before either struck a blow Jack called out from the yard, 'Will, Will Jackson, where are you! Your mistress wants you.'

'I'm sorry, Luke,' said Will, 'I must go.'

'Don't think you've dodged your hiding,' said Luke. 'It's men like you are the ruin of this land.'

Will Jackson hurried to the kitchen and Bridget took him through to the main part of the house. 'In there,' she said, pointing to a door, 'and hurry back to the kitchen.'

Will knocked at the door and was told to enter by Jane Lane. She was sitting on a window seat and Henry Lassells was walking up and down. Will Jackson shut the door.

'Oh, Your Majesty,' said Lassells, 'this is dreadful. That common woman boxing your ears! It is intolerable that you should have to consort with the servants, but Mr Tomes doesn't know who you are.'

'Be quiet, Henry,' said Jane, and then, with laughter in her eyes, she said, 'Will, I am displeased with you. The cook has complained about you to Mr Tomes. She says that you have spoken against the King and that you are a dangerous Parliament man!'

'I am sorry for it, Mistress,' said Will, 'but I cannot help being a law-abiding Englishman. They are all red-hot supporters of the rebel, Charles Stuart!'

Jane Lane stood up and curtsied and then started to laugh.

'Your Majesty,' she said, 'this is most droll. You being boxed on the ear by a cook, and being blamed for speaking against the King!'

'It seemed the best thing to do, the soldier there said I was like the King and began studying my features, so I thought I'd put him off the scent.'

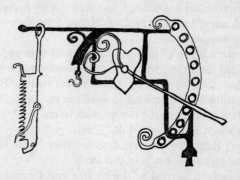

'But, Sire,' said Lassells, 'that you should be struck by a cook!'

'Don't distress yourself,' said the King. 'It was very good for me. No one has ever done that before.'

'We have arranged for a truckle bed to be put in Henry's room, Sire,' said Jane, 'and when all is quiet Henry can use it and Your Majesty can have his bed.'

'And a good thing too,' said the King, 'for I am in considerable danger if I return to the servants' quarters.'

'In danger?' said Jane and Lassells in alarm.

'Yes, in danger of getting a black eye and a bloody nose from a lusty young serving-man named Luke.'

'Heavens above!' said Jane, 'but why?'

'Oh, a slight difference between us. Partly because I spoke

against the King, but mainly because he caught me kissing his girl in the garden!'

'Oh, Sire, you must be careful!' said Jane.

'You know I can never resist a pretty wench, and it is such a lovely night.'

'How dared he!' said Lassells.

'Oh, I admire him for it, but I confess I am glad I have avoided a fight.'

'This is dreadful,' said Lassells.

'On the contrary,' said the King, 'it is magnificent!'

CHAPTER TEN

JULIANA ELOPES

THE next morning Prudence risked the wrath of Bridget and slipped out of the kitchen before her washing-up was finished. She made her way discreetly to the front drive and took up a position behind a thick bush, where she could see the guests leave. She watched Miss Lane and the young gentleman saying good-bye to her master, but her eyes were on Will Jackson the servant, who was waiting demurely by the head of the strawberry roan horse. Then Will mounted and settled into the saddle in front of Miss Lane, and with the young gentleman leading they trotted down the drive.

As they drew level Prudence stepped out from behind the

bush and waved her hand prettily to Will Jackson. Miss Lane was looking back to wave to Mr Tomes, so Will was able to turn his head, unperceived by his mistress. He grinned cheerfully and gave her a large wink. Then he looked to his front, the demure and well-behaved serving-man.

Prudence watched them turn out of the drive into the road, watched their heads above the hedge, and when they turned a bend and went out of sight she sighed deeply.

'There he goes,' she said to herself. 'I'll never see him again. So handsome and friendly, almost as if he were one of the gentry! What did he say – "Kissed by the King of England!" Full of jests he was. If he is like the King, as they said, then what fools men are these days!'

She stood dreaming of the handsome servant until she was brutally brought to her senses by the furious voice of Bridget. 'Prudence Pottleeton! What are you doing, wench! Come you here, at once!' Prudence hurried back to the kitchen, had her ears boxed, and continued washing up. But throughout the day, and from time to time for many a year afterwards, she dreamed of that moment in the rose-scented garden and the tall, dark, young man, who they said was like the King.

Jane Lane and Lassells with their servant travelled thirty-six miles that day, through Chipping Camden to Cirencester, with Lord Wilmot and Colonel Lane following ten miles behind them. Twice they were stopped by soldiers, but each time Jane's pass allowed them to go on their way. The soldiers found Miss Lane and Mr Lassells quite above suspicion, and their servant a cheerful fellow with a friendly word. At Cirencester they stayed at the Sun Inn and a truckle bed was provided in Lassells' room for the serving-man.

After Cirencester Colonel Lane went off to London, to see if he could make contact with friends of the King, and Lord Wilmot followed the others more closely. They rode through Chipping Sodbury and on to Bristol, which promised to be the most hazardous part of their journey. They had to go through the city to get to Abbots Leigh, a country house three miles beyond Bristol where the King was to stay for a few days.

As they rode through the Lawford Gate they steeled themselves for the ordeal. They had only travelled along open roads until then, and there was a serious risk that among the hundreds of people in the streets someone might recognize the King. The only way was to ride boldly and naturally through the streets, ready to make a dash for safety if disaster occurred. But the people of Bristol took no particular notice. Will Jackson rode the strawberry roan with careful correctness, winding in and out of the traffic, looking neither to the right nor to the left. They crossed on the ferry to the other side of the river, and began to feel safe when they came to the handsome church of St Mary Redcliffe. Soon they passed through the Redcliffe gate on to the open road. Partly with relief, and partly to get to the safety of Abbots Leigh quickly, they broke into an easy canter.

Three miles down the road they turned off into the grounds of Abbots Leigh, and saw Sir George Norton and some friends playing bowls. The players looked up in surprise and Sir George came forward. He recognized the King at once, but quickly took a warning sign and said nothing. Jane and Lassells were introduced to the others, and then Sir George took the King to a little room at the back of the house and made him welcome. To avoid awkward questions it was announced that Miss Lane's servant was ill and was in bed, and the King stayed safely out of sight for the four days they were there.

Every day Lord Wilmot and Lassells went to Bristol on the difficult mission of trying to find a ship to take the King to France. They had to seek out Royalists, meet them secretly, find reliable ship-owners and, without giving any information away, sound them about taking a 'gentleman' secretly to France. After four days Wilmot realized that there was no chance of success. Bristol was too closely controlled by the army. So it was decided to go on to the south of Somerset, to the home of a reliable Royalist gentleman named Colonel Wyndham at Trent. From there they could try to find a boat

going from the south coast. Lord Wilmot went first, to warn
Colonel Wyndham that the King was coming.

The King left Abbots Leigh early in the morning, riding as
before in front of Jane Lane, with Henry Lassells at their side.
They were anxious at first, riding out in the open after the
relatively safe seclusion of Abbots Leigh, though Yorick
showed that for his part he was glad to be out of the stable
again.

It was a lovely day, with a tang of autumn in the air and
touches of gold and brown in the green of trees and hedges,
and soon the King became cheerful.

'Bless us all!' he said. 'This is mighty pleasant, riding
quietly through the mellow sunshine without a care in the
world!'

'Without a care in the world, Your Majesty!' said Lassells in
surprise.

'Why yes, young man, what cares have I? Unless you count
Noll Cromwell and his solemn soldiers, which I do not; I don't
care that for them!' He snapped his fingers.

'Bravely spoken, sir,' said Jane.

'Let us sing,' the King said. 'A round, to pass the time. Jane,
you sing second and Henry third, and keep time I beg of you.'
At once he started, in his rich and tuneful voice:

'My dame hath a lame tame crane,
  My dame hath a crane which is lame
Pray, gentle Jane, let my dame's lame tame crane
  Feed and come home again!'

When the King had sung the first line Jane sang it while he
sang the second, but although the King waved his hand and
jerked his head at Lassells the young man remained silent,
blushing with embarrassment.

'Cornet Lassells, sing the third part,' the King said.

'But, Your Majesty, I cannot,' he said.

'You cannot? Nonsense, man, everyone can sing.'

E

'I think, Sire,' said Jane, 'that poor Henry thinks it disrespectful to sing with you.'

'Fiddlesticks, boy,' the King said, 'I command you to sing.'

'And if the King commands it, Henry,' said Jane, 'as a dutiful subject and as a cornet in the army, then sing you must.'

'But, Sire,' said Lassells, 'what if we meet someone!'

'If they ride our way then they shall join in, if they meet us what could better testify to the innocence of our journey than to be singing light-heartedly as we go! So let us sing.'

'As Your Majesty commands,' said Lassells, not very happily.

'Nay, as Will Jackson asks you,' said the King with his quick and friendly smile, 'we will take our time from the rhythm of Yorick's pace.'

'My dame hath a lame tame crane ...' he sang again, and this time first Jane and then Lassells joined in, and they sang it until they got into such a hopeless tangle with the words that they broke down in laughter. Then they sang 'Three Blind Mice' and 'Christchurch Bells'. From rounds they got to ballads and the King sang some old French songs his mother had taught him when he was very young. It was all very happy and pleasant, and they stopped for a picnic lunch of tongue and new-baked bread they had brought with them.

In the middle of the afternoon they reached Castle Carey, where Lord Wilmot had arranged for the King to spend the night at the Manor House, the home of Mr Kirton. The King was still in his gay mood, and after supper they all played cards far into the night, so that the candles had to be renewed several times.

From Castle Carey they rode another ten miles to Trent. As they drew near to the imposing mansion amid its wide parkland they met Colonel Wyndham and his wife, who had come to meet them. The King became Will Jackson the servant, and looked demurely down his nose when they met, but as soon as he was in his own apartments Colonel Wyndham and his wife kissed his hand.

'We were exceedingly anxious, Your Majesty,' said Wyndham, 'and feared that disaster had overtaken you.'

'No disaster, Colonel, in fact we have had a most pleasant journey.'

'Here you will be safe, Sire,' said Mrs Wyndham. 'We have prepared this suite of rooms for you, and I hope they will be suitable. The small walled garden there is quite private, and if there is an alarm, we have a secret room behind the fireplace.'

'Let me show Your Majesty how it is entered,' said Wyndham. He lifted a picture and showed a panel which slid back, making an aperture through which an agile man could slip. Inside was a narrow room built into the wall, with light from a concealed grating. It was furnished with a small bed, a chair, and a table.

'There is a way out on the other side, Sire,' Wyndham explained, 'through a trap-door into the garden.'

'This is splendid, my dear Colonel,' the King said, 'and at last I can live in comfort, though I hope it will not be long before we find a ship to take me to France. Until then, I shall be your very grateful guest.'

The King spent five days at Trent, living more as befitted his rank. The task of Jane Lane and Henry Lassells was completed, and it was decided that they should go back to Bentley Hall. They went to say good-bye to the King, and kissed his hand.

'Good-bye, Mistress Jane,' he said, 'and a safe journey back to your home. This time you will not be burdened with a servant who is both clumsy at his duties and a sore risk to your safety.'

'It has been an experience I shall never forget, Sire, and an honour I cherish.'

'One day, Mistress, I hope to be able to show your family how much I value their devotion. We must not forget Yorick, who has carried us so well. I have an idea,' he added, his eyes sparkling, 'that horse must be duly honoured for his loyal service. Yes, your family shall have a new crest to your coat of arms.'

'A strawberry roan horse, Sire? That would be magnificent.'

'Yes, but we must be properly heraldic over this. Let me see. "The crest a demi-horse, strawberry colour, bridled sable, bitted and garnished or." That would be the head and shoulders of the horse, strawberry colour, with a black bridle and a gold bit. But there must be the mark of royalty. Yes, we'll have it "supporting an imperial crown gold". So your horse shall hold in his fore-legs a royal crown.'

'It is a charming device, Your Majesty, and a reminder for all time of the service our family were able to do for you. He is such a nice horse, too!'

'One day, when times are normal, I shall command the College of Heralds to issue the warrant. For now, bear that crest. And Cornet Lassells, I thank you, too.'

'Your Majesty, it was a proud duty. I wish I could continue with you.'

'Nay, you must escort Mistress Jane to her home. Perhaps, before long, we may meet again, and I promise you promotion and whatsoever my favour can do for you.'

'I want no reward, Sire. To have you safely here is enough.'

'Poor Henry Lassells,' said the King with a smile, 'I don't know which you disliked most, the risk of being taken or having me hold your stirrup for you! Now, go both of you to Bentley Hall, and I shall wait here until we find a ship and then, God willing, to France!'

While the King played at cards, or petted the spaniels, read or listened to the lute played by Wyndham's niece, Juliana Coningsby, Colonel Wyndham and Lord Wilmot travelled about in the search of news of a ship. They went to Salisbury, where there were many Royalists, and tried Southampton and the ports near by. But the days passed with no success.

One evening he was playing picquet with Mrs Wyndham,

while Juliana sat with her embroidery, when they heard the bells of the village church pealing joyously. They were being rung with unusual vigour as though in celebration of the news of a great victory. Juliana went to find out from the servants what had happened. She came back with Lord Wilmot and Colonel Wyndham, and they were all smiling.

'News, Your Majesty,' said Juliana. 'Uncle here has had success at last. He has found a ship to take you to France. But there is no need. Alas, Sire, you are dead!'

'I am *dead*?' said the King. 'What did I die of?'

'The axe, Sire! They have just received the news in the village, and the servants have it. Charles Stuart was captured three days ago in Bristol and he has been executed by order of the Council.'

The King stood up, looking very solemn. 'Alas! Poor young man! Let us respect his memory and, as the tradition is, declare, "The King is dead, long live the King"!'

'There was another rumour, Sire, in Salisbury,' said Wilmot. 'I was told by several people that you had been captured dressed as a fish-wife, with a cushion down your shirt to make you fat, and that you died bravely.'

'Ah well, let us hope they don't have to ring the bells again. I confess I am sad to hear the vigour with which your bell-ringers celebrate my death. But what is this talk of a ship?'

'There is a vessel at Charmouth, Your Majesty,' said Wyndham, 'owned by a certain Captain Limbry. He has agreed to take you to France for sixty pounds.'

'Oh, excellent. Does he know who his passenger is?'

'A Royalist gentleman is all I said. He is, I think, a safe man, sir. The long-boat will be waiting to take you to the ship at midnight tomorrow.'

'How far is it to Charmouth?'

'About twenty-two miles, sir.'

'An easy ride. Do you send a trusty servant to take rooms for us at Charmouth. How shall I travel this time? Jane Lane has gone, and if I am a servant, whose shall it be?'

'We must have a reason for the journey, sir,' said Lord Wilmot.

'And it must be something to allay suspicion,' said Colonel Wyndham. 'Juliana, my dear, you are the clever one, what would be safest for His Majesty?'

'I shall come myself, as far as Charmouth,' said Juliana. 'The wits of a woman might stand you in good stead, sir. But the reason? What can that be? I have it,' she said, 'Henry Wilmot and I are lovers, and we are eloping!'

'What!' said Lord Wilmot, 'you are eloping with me?'

'Yes, Henry, do you mind?'

'I am enchanted, Mistress, but how does this help His Majesty to elude his enemies?'

'Juliana is right,' said the King, 'and I love a romance. Yes, you are eloping, I am your servant. We must be secret, stay in our rooms, avoid crowds and questioning. The elopement provides the reason. If anyone is suspicious we have an excellent excuse. How is it?' he said, looking thoughtful. 'Yes, Juliana is an orphan, her father and mother are dead. She is a rich heiress with a cruel and grasping guardian. Henry here is her true love and they are running away from the guardian! How's that?'

'Very pat and neat, Sire,' said Juliana, 'and a good reason for our secretive conduct.'

'So be it,' said Lord Wilmot, 'and if I have to elope with a young lady, there's no one I would rather have than you, Mistress.' He bowed gallantly and she curtsied.

'And I am your obedient servant,' said the King.

It was late afternoon when Juliana Coningsby, with the King riding before her, Lord Wilmot, and Colonel Wyndham rode carefully down the steep stony road into the little town of Charmouth. They went along the main street, which was unusually full of people in holiday mood, and Wyndham asked someone why there was such a bustle.

'Why, where be you from? You must be strangers indeed!

'Tis fair-day in Lyme, a mile down the road, and folks have come in from all about,' said the man.

'Ah, I see,' said Wyndham. 'I thank you, friend.' He rode on quickly to avoid further questions and the man stood looking after him, puzzled at such ignorance.

'There's a piece of bad luck,' said the King. 'We must have a care. Where is the inn?'

'It is the Queen's Head, Sire. My servant will have engaged

rooms. But I doubt not that the inn will be full, because of the fair.'

'It cannot be helped. Let us first ride along to the beach to see the ship. 'Tis a sight I have long wanted to see.'

They turned down a steep pathway, turned a corner made by the cliff-edge, and stopped. Two hundred yards or so off the shore lay a two-masted ship.

'There she is, sir,' said Wilmot.

'Yes, there she is,' said the King, 'and beyond her the horizon, and beyond the horizon – France and safety. At last!'

'The captain is to come to this point at midnight, sir,' said Wyndham. 'I will come down here an hour or so before and wait. As soon as he comes I will fetch you from the inn.'

'It seems a pity to go away,' said the King.

'If we all wait here for six hours,' said Juliana, 'it is sure to arouse suspicion. Someone will come. We must play our parts and go to the Queen's Head. We can have supper and pass the time as best we can.'

'We will leave the horses saddled,' said Lord Wilmot, 'then if anything goes amiss we can get away quickly.'

'Come then,' said the King. He looked again at the ship, then turned the horse's head and led the way up the path to Charmouth.

CHAPTER ELEVEN

SHOD IN THREE COUNTIES

IT required courage to ride into the crowded yard of the Queen's Head. It was the only thing to do, for strangers waiting about would be sure to be noticed, and above all they had to avoid arousing curiosity. They dismounted in the yard and the King, encouraged by the nearness of his delivery, acted his part with confidence. He called for the ostler and the landlord, holding the horses' heads while the others waited.

The ostler hurried up and the men sitting on the benches drinking ale looked at the newcomers with idle interest. Then a woman came out of a side-door.

'Who's calling for the landlord?' she asked.

'I am, Mistress,' said the King. 'My master here, the young lady, and their friend have ordered rooms to be prepared.'

'My servant came to arrange it,' said Wyndham.

'I'm the landlady, Margaret Wade, at your service. My husband is busy inside. The rooms are prepared. But if you will be so kind, sir, as to take your supper in the public room it would be doing me a favour, seeing it's Lyme fair-day and we are overrun with custom.'

'Sorry, Mistress,' said Lord Wilmot, 'but we want to be private. That is why we spoke for the rooms in advance.' He turned to the King. 'Will, see that the horses are fed and watered, loosen the girths, but keep the saddles on, in case we have to leave quickly. Join us in our rooms when you have done.'

'Very good, sir,' said the King, with a bow.

Wilmot, Wyndham, and Juliana went off and followed the landlady up the wooden stairs to the gallery on to which the rooms opened. The King led the horses into loose-boxes, and went to fetch the ostler, who had disappeared. He saw him talking to a sergeant of Militia and the man they had spoken to when they came into the town. It was clear that they were discussing the new arrivals. The landlady came down the stairs, and the sergeant beckoned her. She joined the conference. The sergeant was asking questions and began to look important. He stood up and tightened his belt. The King went across to them.

'Saving your presence, Mistress,' he said, 'could the ostler give me oats for the horses?'

'You're the servant of the party who have just come, aren't you?' she said.

'Will Jackson, Mistress, at your service.'

'Where do you come from?' the sergeant said.

'Well, Sergeant, my orders are to say nothing to anyone about that.'

'Oh indeed,' said the sergeant, 'and is your master's journey so secret then?'

The King assumed an air of embarrassment. Then he looked round to make sure that no one was listening, and spoke in a low voice.

'There's a good reason,' he said, 'my master and the young lady are – running away.'

'What are they running away from?' the sergeant asked.

'I should not say, but, if you will promise to keep it to yourselves, they are lovers.'

'Oh, lovers,' said the landlady with new interest. 'I see.'

'They are eloping,' said the King. 'The young lady has no parents, and a harsh-tempered guardian who has a mind to her inheritance. She and my master are true lovers and – you understand now why they wish to be private, and keep the horses saddled?'

'And may God bless them,' said the landlady, 'I'll go and see to the supper myself. True love, especially in adversity, is a beautiful thing!' She hurried off.

The sergeant unfastened his belt and sat down. 'And here was I thinking they were Royalists, running from justice. I thought the young man was a nobleman in disguise, on the run from Worcester fight! Off with you, ostler, and see to the horses. And as for you, Will or whatever your name is, rest assured I'll not disturb them. What's more if that unnatural old guardian comes let me know and we'll see to him. Lovers!' he said, laughing delightedly, 'and I thought they were run-aways from Worcester!'

'You can never be sure, these days, Sergeant,' said the King.

'That's a certain fact, my lad,' the sergeant said. 'Join me for a pint pot of ale when you have finished your duties.'

'If I have the time I will, Sergeant, and thank you,' the King said and went back to the stable.

The ostler was filling buckets with water for the horses. 'Take the oats from that bin at the end there,' he said to the King, 'there's a measure inside.'

When the King brought the oats and tipped them in the manger the ostler said, 'I've seen you before somewhere, friend, though I can't for the life of me think where. Ever been to Exeter?'

'Aye, I was in service with a gentleman there several years back,' the King said.

'That must have been it. D'you know why I went and told the sergeant about your master?'

'No? You were right to be suspicious, it's our duty these days to keep our wits about us.'

'I always have sharp wits. The reason I went was because there was something queer about it all. The way your master and the other gentleman looked about them, the way they insisted on a private room, telling you to keep the horses saddled, and so on. It shows my instincts were right. I thought it was political, and there are good rewards going to the man who uses his eyes. None of those slippery gentry will get past me if they come this way.'

'I wager they won't,' said the King, who was rubbing down Lord Wilmot's horse.

'They do say that Charles Stuart himself may be lurking in the west country here,' the ostler said.

'They say he's everywhere! Hello, this off-fore shoe is loose. Is there a smith near?'

'There's Hamnet, but he's gone to Lyme to the fair. He'll be at his forge in the morning.'

'Then Hamnet must shoe my master's horse.'

'I'll see to it, friend. Yes, that's what they say, that Charles Stuart is in these parts. If he came here I'd know him, at once, like that!' He snapped his fingers sharply.

'Have you seen him, then?'

'Me seen him? Why, a score of times. In the Rebellion, and at Worcester. I was at that battle, you know.'

'Were you?' said the King with admiration, which the ostler noticed and liked.

'Yes, I was, and I chased them into the city, and out the other side. How they ran, those wild Scots and the few rene-gade English that were with them. As for Charles Stuart he's a man of your colouring, only three or four fingers taller than you, and not so human-looking, if you understand me.'

'Well, good luck to you, friend, if he does come this way. A thousand pounds is a nice prize to win.'

'And gladly I'd take it. The trouble he's caused. No one wants him.'

'No, I don't suppose they do. Well, the horses are rubbed down and watered and fed. I must go and wait on my master.'

'If you get time, come down and find me and we'll have a pot of ale together. I like you.'

'Thank you, I'll see if I can manage it. And, friend, don't tell anyone about my master eloping. Word might get round and spoil all.'

'I'll not betray you!'

The King went up to the gallery, met the landlady, ex-changed a friendly smile with her as confederates, and was taken to the rooms reserved for his master and his friends. The landlady was carrying a tray of food, a cold ham, bread, and ale, and she gave it to the servant, smiled in a kind way at Wilmot and Juliana, and went out. Wyndham and Wilmot quickly took the tray from the King, who sat down.

'I have had a very busy quarter of an hour,' he said, and he told them what had happened.

'But, sir,' said Juliana, 'that was highly dangerous.'

'If I hadn't plunged in heaven knows what would have happened,' he said. 'That sergeant would have fetched an officer and all might have been lost. Now they all think they are in our secret, and are delighted with the situation. I confess, though, that the ostler made my hair stand on end at times. However, we are good friends now. It would be better, I think, if I kept my room. Drinking ale with the sergeant and that ostler might lead to my undoing. I wish it was time to go to that ship.'

'The tide doesn't turn until an hour before dawn, sir,' said Wilmot.

'I'll go down to the beach and keep my eyes open for the sea captain,' said Wyndham.

'Yes, a good idea,' said the King, 'and come and let us know directly he comes. I desire more than anything else to set foot on the deck of that ship. Perhaps this time tomorrow we shall be in France!'

'God willing, sir,' said Lord Wilmot.

The evening dragged by. There was singing in the yard below, and the landlady and her potman passed backwards and forwards constantly with pots of ale. Some jugglers came to sleep in a stable and gave a performance to the delight of the revellers. Wilmot and Juliana kept watch at the window and the King sat at the table, sipping his glass of wine and drumming anxiously with his fingers on the arm of the chair. When darkness fell some people went away, but many stayed and there was always someone about.

The three people waiting so anxiously found little to say.

Candles were lighted and snuffed from time to time. It grew cold and they lit the fire, time dragged more slowly, and gradually they began to be anxious.

'I should have thought he would have come by now,' the King said as the sky began to lighten in the east.

'I expect the captain is leaving it to the last minute for safety,' said Wilmot, but he, too, was watching the entrance to the yard fixedly. Juliana had fallen asleep on the settle by the fire.

Dawn had broken when at last Wilmot said, 'Here he is!'

'At last!' said the King. He picked up his cloak and fastened it at the throat. Juliana got up and put on her cloak. Wilmot went to the door to unlock it for Colonel Wyndham. They heard him running up the stairs two at a time. Wilmot opened the door and closed it as soon as Wyndham was inside the room.

'He hasn't come, Your Majesty,' he said.

They all looked at him in silence.

'But – why not?' said the King.

'I don't know, Sire. No message, nothing. And the tide has turned. If he came now it would be too late to sail – before this evening.'

'If he's been taken, or proved false,' said Wilmot, 'they'll be after us. You must get away from here, sir, at once.'

The King was standing at the window, looking towards the sea. He turned away sadly. 'I thought it was all over,' he said, 'but – the hunt is up once more. Where now?'

'Back to Trent, Your Majesty,' said Colonel Wyndham, 'if you will. I can offer you sanctuary as safe as any, and we can seek a ship again.'

'It is good of you, Wyndham,' said the King, 'and I accept your hospitality – though I mislike going back anywhere.'

'It would be wiser, Sire,' said Juliana, 'not to go back on our tracks from here, if they have been alarmed they may know by which road we came into the town.'

'We'll take the coast road,' said Wyndham, 'to Bridport,

and then on towards Dorchester. We can turn off that road later and make our way across country to Trent.'

'I'll stay behind for a few hours,' said Wilmot, 'in case there is a message from Captain Limbry.'

'Your horse needs a smith, by the way,' said the King. 'Where shall we meet you, Henry?'

'You had best go to the George Inn, Sire, and if I don't join you there, I'll meet you outside the town on the road to Dorchester.'

'Good. Then all is arranged, and the sooner we go the better. I will go down first and get the horses out. As soon as I have tightened the girths and got them ready, come down. Henry can settle with the landlady.'

The King led out the two horses as quietly as he could, while Lord Wilmot went down to the beach to see if the captain had come. But two horses coming from their stable into a cobbled yard make a great deal of noise at half past four in the morning, and as Juliana and Wyndham came down the steps the ostler came out of a door at the end of the stables, rubbing his eyes and yawning.

'Hi, what's afoot?' he said.

'My master's friend and the lady have decided to continue their journey,' said the King, helping Juliana to mount.

'What about the bill?'

'My friend will pay that, he is following later,' said Wyndham.

'And please remember to take his horse to the smith,' said the King; 'here, this is for the cost, use the change for yourself.'

'Thank you, friend,' said the ostler. He looked at the coin in his hand, spat on it, and put it away. 'You're very generous. But why are you going at this time of the morning?'

'Oh, have done with your questioning, man!' said Wyndham sharply. 'Mount, Will, and let us begone!'

The King mounted, gathered up the reins, and the two horses walked out of the yard. The ostler stood staring at them.

Then he scratched his head, pulled some straws from his hair, and walked slowly back to his shed.

An hour later he led Lord Wilmot's horse to the smithy, where Hamnet the smith was heating up his furnace with the bellows.

'You're early,' he said.

'A gentleman wants to be on the road early. The off-fore is loose.'

While the ostler held the horse the smith examined the off-fore shoe. 'Aye, he'd have cast it in half an hour. I'll have a look at the others, just to be sure. Why, that's strange; that's very peculiar indeed!' he said when he had looked at the three other hooves.

'What's strange?'

Hamnet sat on his stool and picked up a horseshoe, examining it to see that it would do. Then he looked at the ostler. 'This horse has been shod in three counties – and one of them Worcestershire! That's what's strange, my friend!'

'Can you tell that, just from looking at the shoes?'

'Of course I can. Every county has its different ways of shoeing. 'Tis a long journey this gentleman of yours has made, and it is odd that he comes from Worcester!'

'You mean, the battle that was there?'

'That's exactly what I do mean. From what they say there are gentlemen and nobles scattered far and wide hiding themselves from the righteous vengeance of the Lord Protector. Moreover, they tend to make for the sea-shore. What manner of a gentleman was this? Young?'

'Youngish, rather grand in his bearing. You know, smith, there's more than the shoeing that is strange. They behaved very secret-like when they came ...'

'They? Were there several of them then?'

'Yes, this gentleman and a young lady, and another gentleman and a servant, a fellow named Will Jackson. But they explained, or this Will did, that they were runaway lovers. They left this morning, an hour ago, of a sudden, except the gentleman who owns this horse. Now why should runaway lovers leave of a sudden? No one had come to startle them, no angry guardian I mean.'

'Runaways, yes,' said the smith, 'but lovers or traitors? That's the question. Did you notice anything else about them? What was the other gentleman like?'

'Oh, just a gentleman, spoke sharp-like. But there was something about the servant, Will Jackson. He was tall, more than six foot I should say ...'

'What's that?' said the smith, 'more than two yards high? He hadn't got dark hair, had he, and a sallow complexion?'

'Yes, that's right.'

'There's a piece of paper nailed to the church door,' said Hamnet slowly, 'bidding all true men to seek a young fellow more than two yards high with dark hair and a sallow visage! That man is Charles Stuart!'

They looked at each other.

'But this fellow was a servant. He talked to me as easy as you like. Why, we even talked about catching the King!'

'By all accounts he's as wily as a fox and cunning as a serpent,' said the smith. 'Look how he's tricked the whole army for three weeks, and everyone a-hunting him.'

'Wait a minute,' said the ostler, 'I thought I'd seen him somewhere. It *is* him! I mind now where it was, it was at Worcester, and before that I saw him at Bristol, oh, six years ago when he was a lad of fifteen or so, in a special suit of armour. And there was I talking to him!'

'There's a thousand pounds reward for giving information leading to his capture. Half for you and half for me.'

The smith had shod the horse as he talked, and now it put its hoof to the ground, scraping it tentatively.

'What do we do?' said the ostler.

'Best tell the parson and he can tell the soldiers. I don't like to have to do with them, you never know when they're going to enlist you.'

'There's another thing. When he went he gave me a crown,

a whole silver crown, to pay for your shoeing. That's out of all reason.'

'Just the sort of thing he would do, not knowing any better. Take this horse, and get you gone to the parson at once. If they lay this wicked man by the heels we shall be doing our duty, and we shall be rich.'

'I'll go at once,' said the ostler.

'Yes, he's the one. You'll find him at home. He can tell the soldiers. Pay me for the shoeing later. If this horse could talk, I wager he could tell us a tale, eh, old chap?' The smith slapped the horse's flank and the ostler led him back to the stables in the yard of the Queen's Head. Then he hurried up the street to the parsonage.

The King, Wyndham, and Juliana were riding along the road to Bridport at a good steady trot.

'I'd like to know what kept that sea captain,' the King said.

'There are a dozen reasons, sir,' said Juliana.

'And one only which I like not – that he has told the soldiers!'

'There is no sign of any pursuit,' Juliana said, looking back along the road, which from the crest of the hill they had topped could be seen for a long way.

'If they do find that I am in this part of the country they'll cordon it off and hunt me with every man they have got.'

'Come, sir, you have outwitted them so far, you can continue to do so.'

'I expect so, but good fortune does not hold for ever, and it is a wearisome business, being the quarry.'

'He may have taken ill, sir, or been prevented from going to his ship by some unforeseen event. They may know nothing about you.'

'I hope you are right, Juliana,' he said, 'but I have a feeling that all is not well.'

CHAPTER TWELVE

'BROTHER ROUNDHEAD'

LORD WILMOT went back to the Queen's Head from the beach to pay the reckoning and follow the King. He found the landlady by the door in angry conversation with a lean sour-looking parson. The first words he heard made Wilmot shrink back to listen unperceived.

'That's a fine tale, Parson Wesley,' she was saying, 'but what proof have you that it is true?'

'Adequate proof, Mistress Wade,' said the parson. 'Hamnet, the smith, noticed that one of their horses had been shod recently in three counties, and one of them Worcester. Their conduct was highly suspicious and now your ostler remembers one of them.'

'Pouf! that's naught to go by, man,' she said. 'I won't believe they were Royalists.'

'There is more, Mistress! They had with them a servant, a tall dark-visaged fellow, is not that so?'

'They did. He was a handsome young fellow that I liked as soon as I saw him. What of him?'

'You liked him, eh?' said the parson triumphantly. 'Then I will tell you that that servant was Charles Stuart himself, self-styled King and the arch enemy of the people!'

'It's not possible!' she said.

'It was undoubtedly the rebel, Charles Stuart. Yes,' he said harshly, 'Charles Stuart slept last night at your house, and by that are you condemned for harbouring a wicked young man!'

The landlady drew herself up and put her hands on her hips. Her eyes flashed. 'If I thought it was the King, as you say it was, I would think the better of myself all the days of my life, and blessed by having helped His Majesty. And so, Mr Parson, get you out of my house or else I'll get those shall kick you out! Go on, begone!'

The parson hesitated, saw the look in her eyes, and began to go. Then he stopped. 'See,' he said, 'here are those will cure you of your wicked tongue!'

An officer came into the inn, with a sergeant at his heels and a score of men who halted outside.

'Bah! I care not for Captain Mercer of the Militia,' she said, and turned on her heels and went. Lord Wilmot snapped his fingers and she went over to him, unseen by the parson who was talking to the officer.

'Bless you, good Mistress, for your stout heart,' said Wilmot. 'I shall tell the young man you spoke of, and he, too, will bless you. I must fly now, to warn him. Here, this is for the account!'

'Was it the King, sir?' she said.

'Perhaps,' said Wilmot, 'perhaps it was the King of England!'

'Gramercy, if I'd known, he'd have had that fat pheasant I had by me, cooked in white wine, spiced and flavoured by my own hands!'

She curtsied to Lord Wilmot and went off. He turned his attention to the officer and the parson.

'That signifies nothing, Master Wesley, nothing at all,' the officer was saying. 'We are not interested in stupid women. Besides, we all know Mistress Wade. Nay, it is the royal quarry we want. You are sure of all you have told me?'

'You can ask the ostler yourself, Captain, but I do think you should arrest Mistress Wade for her scandalous speech to me.'

'I don't want to waste time with the ostler. It sounds most like him, and there was a brig lying off the coast all night. Sergeant!'

'Sir!'

'Go at once to the colonel and report what you have heard. Tell him we are searching the country within marching distance to the east. Say that the rebels are reported to have ridden towards Bridport, Charles Stuart disguised as a servant riding before a young lady on a grey mare, accompanied by one or two men.' He turned to the parson. 'When did they leave, d'you say?'

'About an hour ago it seems.'

'Tell the colonel that, Sergeant, and hurry.'

'Yes, sir,' said the sergeant, and he went. A corporal came in and took his place beside the officer.

'That's all we can do, Parson. Doubtless a squadron of horse will be sent after them at once, and others will be sent on patrol inland. Now we will see if they have gone to earth near by. That man is cunning enough for anything.'

Lord Wilmot had heard all he needed to know. He slipped out into the yard, fetched his horse, mounted, and trotted out into the street before the ostler or the soldiers realized it. Some ran after him, all shouted, but he set spurs to his horse and went down the steep road out of Charmouth at a gallop. He rode as fast as his horse would go and covered the nine miles to Bridport in a very short time.

He had to slow down to a walk in the town, for it was full of soldiers, being mustered to go on an expedition. The yard of the George Inn was full of them, and he dismounted, wondering where he would find the King. His heart went cold of a sudden, for he saw the other two horses tethered to a post. With the place so full of soldiers and in such a bustle of excitement it seemed that the worst had happened.

While Wilmot was wondering whether it would be any use trying to fight his way in to try to rescue the King, he saw him. He was pushing his way through the soldiers, exchanging cheerful greetings. Wilmot put up his hand to catch the King's attention, and at that moment a groom saw him and held out his hand.

'Welcome, friend,' he said to the King, 'I know your face! We've met before.'

'I'm sure we have,' the King said cheerfully. 'How is it with you?'

'Oh, well enough,' said the groom, 'come to my cubby-hole and drink a pot with me, you can remind me where we have met.'

'I will. So go you and get the ale.'

The ostler went off whistling, and as soon as he was out of hearing the King said, 'Well, Henry, what's amiss? Why did not the captain come?'

'There's more urgent matters, Sire. They are after us, or soon will be. A confounded sharp-eyed smith noticed that my horse had been shod in three counties, and Worcester one of them. They put two and two together – and found the right answer. The hue and cry is out, sir. We must go at once.'

'So be it! Go and fetch Wyndham and Juliana, they are in the room at the end, over there. I'll lead these two horses out into the road, you bring yours.'

Within three minutes they were outside the inn, mounted, and making their way down the street, the King playing the part of a good servant and shouting boldly, 'Make way there, make way for a lady; make way I say!'

When they were clear of the soldiers they put their horses

to a canter and rode through the town and out on the Dorchester road. Here Wilmot reined in his horse and waited
under a tree at a corner on top of a long hill to watch the road
behind, while the rest rode on. Soon he galloped after the
King, the others slowed down to let him come up, and he said,
'A score of horsemen riding fast have topped the hill behind.
They'll overtake us in ten minutes or less.'

'They've wasted no time,' said the King.

'Sir,' said Wyndham, 'a hundred yards ahead is a lane to the
left. It will take us across country towards Yeovil.'

'Then we will turn off to the left,' said the King, and they
rode forward to the lane, turned left-handed, and went in
single file down a sharp hill. The lane soon climbed again and
they stopped under a barn, where they would not easily be seen
from the main road. Soon they saw a cloud of dust moving
along the road from Bridport and then a troop of horsemen
flashed by the end, and went on towards Dorchester.

'Shaken them off, for the moment,' said the King, 'now
forward again, and let us keep to by-ways and lie low.'

They rode inland, swung to the right to avoid the town of
Beaminster, passed through the village of Netherbury, and
pulled up at Broadwindsor. Both horses and riders needed a
rest, so they rode into the yard of the village inn, another
George, and dismounted. Colonel Wyndham called for beer,
and when the landlord came out with four pots he exclaimed
with pleasure.

'It's Colonel Wyndham of Trent!' he said. 'Welcome, sir.
I'm right glad to see you!'

'Where have we met, my good man?' said Wyndham.

'I was in service seven years back, sir, with your cousin,
Richard Wyndham of Park Hall!'

'And now I remember you! Where have you been since
then—here in Broadwindsor?'

'For the past three years I've been here, sir. I served the
King in the wars, and was wounded. Alas that the war fell out
so grievously!'

'This is my brother-in-law,' said Wyndham pointing to Lord Wilmot, 'and the young lady is his niece.'

'Honoured to meet you, sir and mistress,' said the landlord beaming and bowing, 'and I pray you will come inside my humble inn and let my wife prepare your dinner. I promise you it will be good.'

Lord Wilmot glanced at the King, who gave his consent with a nod.

'We shall be happy to do so,' Wilmot said. 'Will, do you tend the horses and then join us – to wait upon us.'

'I will, sir,' said the King.

The landlord was so pleased to have them, and the little inn seemed so safe a place amid the hue and cry, that they spent the night there. Big houses in the neighbourhood were searched vigorously, for soldiers were everywhere. Panelling was torn down, cellars, attics, barns, and lofts were examined, but the insignificant inn at Broadwindsor was left alone, so the King and his companions dined and slept in peace.

At dinner Lord Wilmot told them why Captain Limbry had failed to keep his appointment at Charmouth.

'The poor man was much distressed this morning when he came to his ship. He went home to fetch his best linen and appointments for the cabin, and his wife began to question him.'

'Ah, these wives!' said the King.

'This one would not be put off, or poor Limbry had not the wits. Eventually he had to confess that he was taking two Royalist gentlemen to France and his wife forbade it. She feared disgrace and ruin.'

'Did he then submit to her authority?' the King asked.

'He had no choice, sir,' said Wilmot, 'she took away his breeches and to make doubly sure she locked him in his bedroom! He hammered the door and pleaded with her, but she was adamant. Not until the tide had turned and it was too late did she open the door and restore his breeches.'

'And on that woman rested the safety and perhaps the life of a king!' said Wyndham.

'He should have told her before,' said Juliana.

'But the result is – here we are, on the run,' said the King. 'How much longer will it be! But next time, if there be a next time, we keep the captain with us and see that he does not risk domestic imprisonment!'

The next day they bade farewell to the landlord and his wife and rode across country towards Trent, where the King took up his old quarters with what patience he could muster. He needed patience, for he stayed there more than a week, secretly in his own rooms, while Lord Wilmot and Colonel Wyndham rode to Salisbury and Southampton once more seeking for a ship.

They had no fortune, but friends advised them to seek help on the Sussex coast, and Lord Wilmot brought a friend to Trent to help. He was Colonel Gounter, a lean, tough soldier nearly as tall as the King, and he had many Royalist friends in Hampshire and Sussex. The King said good-bye to Colonel and Mrs Wyndham, and promised to reward them and Juliana Coningsby if he returned. They professed themselves content in having been able to help preserve the King in his adversity.

Colonel Gounter led the way when they left Trent. They skirted Salisbury and rode through Wincanton and Mere to Heal, where the King was expected by Mr Hyde, who owned the mansion there. After one night they left again, as if continuing their journey, but turned northwards and spent the day at Stonehenge. The reason was to allay any suspicion among the servants or people of the neighbourhood, for the King was to spend a week at Heal while arrangements were made for a boat.

The day among the ancient stones of Stonehenge was passed without incident, and in the evening they went back to Heal, entered the house by a back door and into the apartments reserved for him, with a secret hiding place leading from them in case of emergency.

A week later Colonel Gounter brought good news. A sea captain named Tattersall had been found who was willing to take two gentlemen to France from Brighton. He had been told that Lord Wilmot had killed a man in a duel and had to get out of the country, and would be accompanied by his servant. He would make the voyage for sixty pounds and was, it seemed, a most reliable man.

The King, Wilmot, and Gounter left Heal the next day, unnoticed by any of the servants, and rode eastwards into Hampshire. They went by Warnford Down and Old Winchester Hill and as evening drew on they approached Hambledon, where it had been arranged that the King should stay at a large mansion. But it was in such a prominent position that the King asked Gounter if there was not a smaller place where they could pass the night.

'There is my sister's house, Your Majesty,' he said, 'at Broadhalfpenny Down, which is near by. Her husband Thomas Symonds and my sister would be very pleased to see us.'

'Is the house out of the way?' the King asked.

'Yes, indeed, it is most desolate.'

'Then, let us go there.'

Thomas Symonds was out, but his wife, Colonel Gounter's sister, was delighted to welcome her brother and his two friends, 'Mr Barlow' and 'Mr Jackson'. The King had decided not to play the part of a servant but to be a plain gentleman. Lord Wilmot had used the name Barlow whenever he wanted to be unknown.

They had biscuits and wine in the parlour while supper was being prepared, and then all sat at a round table in the dining-room for a splendid meal. They were partly through supper when Thomas Symonds came in. It was at once evident that he had been drinking and he was far from steady on his legs. He stood in the doorway and surveyed the guests at supper.

'Hello!' he said, 'what's this! As soon as my back is turned my wife asks all sorts of riff-raff to supper!'

'Don't be foolish, Tom,' said his wife, 'it is my brother and two friends of his. They are travelling and have come for the night!'

Tom Symonds went to Gounter, peered into his face, and said, 'So it is, and you are welcome.' Then he peered into Lord Wilmot's face, while Gounter introduced him as Mr Barlow. 'And you have the look of an honest man, Barlow,' he said, 'I bid you welcome too. And who is this?'

'A very good friend of mine,' said Colonel Gounter, 'Will Jackson.'

'Will Jackson, eh?' said Symonds, again peering close into his guest's face, 'Well, I don't like you. You have the look of a confounded Roundhead. And I don't want Roundheads in my house!' He turned to Gounter. 'Isn't he a Roundhead, eh?'

'He may be, Tom, but I assure you he's a very good fellow,' said Gounter.

'A good fellow, eh?' He pulled up a chair, sat down next to the King, put an arm round his shoulder, and said, 'Well, Brother Roundhead, we will drink together, and make merry, eh?'

'If it pleases you, sir,' said the King, keeping a very straight face, 'but mark you, no deep drinking, and no swearing!'

'There you are!' said Symonds triumphantly, 'didn't I say he was a Roundhead? No drinking, no swearing! A Puritan, that's what you are. Here, drink this!'

He poured out a glass of wine and gave it to the King, and filled one for himself.

'I give you a toast, Brother Roundhead, and if you don't drink it I'll break your pate! The toast is, "The King, God bless him!"'

The King pretended to hesitate.

'Come, stand up, all of you,' said Symonds, 'and you, Puritan Roundhead, and drink the toast!'

They stood up and they all drank the loyal toast, even 'Brother Roundhead'. Symonds then hurled his glass over his shoulder and it smashed against the wall. Gounter went round to Symonds and took him aside.

'Listen, Tom,' he said, 'let me take this fellow to his room and let him go to bed. Then we can have our revels without him looking down his nose at us. For, in fact, he is a trifle sanctimonious.'

'A good idea, brother-in-law, take him to bed and let us good fellows enjoy ourselves.'

The King was thus able to leave his difficult host, and went to bed, which was very welcome as he had ridden close on forty miles that day.

The next day they rode south-east across Sussex towards Brighton, where Captain Tattersall was to meet them in the George Inn. It was a good fast ride through Arundel and Houghton, and all went well except for one incident. They had

stopped by a little stream to rest their horses and themselves when they saw a large cloud of dust behind them. Soon they saw a large body of horsemen coming along the road. Their instinct was to mount and ride away, but the King stayed them.

'If they see three men riding over the downs away from them their curiosity will be aroused. Let us stay here and watch them pass.'

They assumed natural interest and drew into the side of the road as the cavalry, forty or more, riding fast, swept by them, roughly pushing them aside as they went.

'That is a sight I like not,' said the King; 'let us hope it is not me they are seeking in such haste.'

They rode on quietly after that, to keep the soldiers well in front of them, and topped a rise and saw the sea.

'There it is again,' said the King, 'and this time, I hope, it will not be an empty promise.'

'Amen to that, sir,' said Lord Wilmot.

Colonel Gounter went on to Brighton while the King and Wilmot waited in a little hollow off the road. He came back with the news that all was safe and that they were expected at the George Inn. They set off on the last lap of their journey, seeing no one, and Gounter and the King went up to the sitting-room reserved for them while Lord Wilmot saw to the horses and ordered their supper.

CHAPTER THIRTEEN

THE GEORGE INN AT BRIGHTON

THE King stood at the window of the private room at the George Inn, looking out to sea. The light was fading fast but the evening was so clear that the horizon made a smooth curve, as though it had been ruled with a pair of compasses and a sharp pencil. Beyond the horizon was France – and safety. He sighed.

'What, Your Majesty,' said Colonel Gounter, 'are you melancholy?'

'Yes, Gounter. Because I am – so near and yet so far!'

'Come, Sire, be of good heart! We are safely arrived in Brighton. We have a ship waiting to take you to France. What can go amiss now?'

'A great deal can go amiss, my friend,' said the King, turning from the window. 'For one thing the wind is blowing from the wrong direction to take us across the Channel. For another the sea captain has not come yet, and you know what happened at Charmouth when all was ready save going aboard the ship! Another thing is that four Roundhead soldiers have just sat themselves down on the benches outside the inn and seem to have settled there for the evening. Moreover, Wilmot is a long time downstairs with the landlord!'

'As for Captain Tattersall, Sire,' said Gounter, 'I am convinced he is a man of his word. He will come. And here is Lord Wilmot.'

'What news, Henry?' the King asked as Lord Wilmot came into the room.

'Of Captain Tattersall, Sire – nothing. He has not been here today. And the landlord, a black-visaged giant named Smith, is far from pleased to have us here.'

'He doesn't suspect us?' said the King anxiously.

'Oh no, sir. But he didn't seem very impressed with my story of having to flee the country because of a duel. He said he little liked having a hand in any business likely to get him into trouble with the authorities.'

'Zounds,' said the King, 'if he only knew the business which is afoot, and the trouble he is risking!'

'He is bringing supper, but he can find nothing better than cold salt pork and pease pudding.'

'It will do. I wish your sea captain would come!'

'His Majesty is melancholy, my lord,' said Gounter.

'His Majesty is hungry,' said Lord Wilmot, cheerfully, 'and that depresses a man's spirits. I think I hear Smith the landlord. You had better become my servant, sir, and for safety do not let him see your face.'

When the landlord opened the door Lord Wilmot was sitting in the armchair, Colonel Gounter was at the window, and the King was unpacking a saddle-bag, with his back to the room. The landlord brought a tray of food and began to lay the table.

'When you have taken your supper, sir,' he said to Lord Wilmot, 'I shall be obliged if you will go. I want no hue and cry in my house.'

'We'll go, Mr Smith,' said Wilmot.

The landlord went round the table to arrange plates and happened to look across at the servant unpacking the saddle-bag. He stood quite still, his eyes round with amazement. Then he put down the plate he was holding, muttered an oath, and hurried from the room.

Wilmot sprang up and went to the door, Gounter strode across to his saddle-bag, took out his pistol, and hastily loaded and primed it. The King stood with his hands on his hips, his lips pursed.

'He recognized me!' he said.

'I'm afraid so, sir,' said Wilmot. 'He's gone down the stairs three at a time. What about the window?'

'There are four stalwart soldiers sitting on the bench below drinking ale,' said the King.

'Let's go down at once,' said Gounter, 'and make a dash for the horses.'

'If we do that we are undone,' said the King, 'a brawl is the last thing we want! No, we are trapped. Give me one of your pistols, Gounter, and if the worst comes to the worst we can make a bid for liberty.'

While Colonel Gounter was priming another pistol, Wilmot said, 'He's coming back.'

'Alone?' said the King.

'I think so, sir.'

The King and Colonel Gounter put their pistols behind their backs and Lord Wilmot took his hand from his sword hilt and went back to his chair. They all waited, tense and ready for desperate action if necessary.

The landlord came into the room, closed the door, turned the key, and went towards the King. He dropped on one knee.

'God bless Your Majesty!' he said.

'What do you mean, man?' the King said. 'I am servant to Mr Barlow there!'

'Oh no,' said the landlord, shaking his head, 'I know who you are, Sire! I had the honour of serving in Your Majesty's Life Guard when you were Prince of Wales. I fought under you in the Rebellion. I recognized you at once.'

'It is a heavy secret, landlord,' said Lord Wilmot sharply.

'And quite safe with me, my lord,' said the landlord. 'I remember you now, you are Lord Wilmot.'

The King held out his hand. 'I see it is no good denying myself to you,' he said kindly. 'Come, rise, and let me look at you! My life is in your hands, and it is quite safe, I am convinced of it.'

'It is, sir. I'd give my life rather than betray Your Majesty. I was overcome when I saw you, that is why I hurried away. I have put on a clean apron. I will fetch our finest linen for the table, and our set of silver dishes. And I have fish fresh caught this morning and a tender chicken just roasted. They were for the supper of a Puritan merchant. I hasten, Sire.'

'One moment, friend,' said the King, 'will not the Puritan merchant wonder at his change of fare?'

'Nay, Sire, my wife shall tell him, and no one disputes with her!'

'But do not tell your wife that I am here,' said the King in alarm.

'Never fear, Sire. I will not tell her until your ship is safe over the horizon.'

'Alas, the wind is in the wrong quarter,' said Colonel Gounter.

The landlord looked out of the window. 'Nay, Sire, see – the smoke from the chimney down the road? It has changed. It is a fair wind for France!'

'Zounds, landlord, you are right,' said the King. 'You deserve a knighthood! See Henry, the wind is fair, it could not be better! Hurry, landlord, bring your supper, and a bottle of your best wine, for you shall drink with us. I was melancholy, but now, by thunder, I am as merry as a schoolboy! Hurry, landlord.'

'Yes, yes, Your Majesty. Oh, what a day for the George Inn!'

He bowed, walked backwards to the door, bowed again, and went.

As the landlord had promised, supper was served on a fine linen tablecloth, and the King used the special silver dishes. After supper their final doubts were cleared when word was brought that Captain Tattersall had arrived and was asking to see a Mr Barlow. With some difficulty the landlord was persuaded that he must ignore the King, who would revert to his role of servant to Lord Wilmot. They insisted that he should stay with them, in case he should be tempted to tell his wife the golden news which so excited him.

Thus it was that when Captain Tattersall was shown into the room both Wilmot and Colonel Gounter were sitting down

F

and 'Will Jackson' was standing respectfully in the background. The landlord managed to avoid turning his back on the servant but Tattersall only gave him a glance.

'Glad I am to see you, Captain,' said Wilmot. 'I wondered if something had happened.'

'All is in order, sir,' said Tattersall. He stood with his feet apart, as though on the heaving deck of a ship. His face was weather-beaten and he spoke in a rich Sussex dialect.

'You know why this voyage must be secret, of course?'

'Yes, sir, because of a duel, sir, which proved fatal, so that you must fly the country. Yes, and so long as it was a matter of honour between gentlemen, and all was fair, then I've naught against that.'

'My servant will travel with me,' said Wilmot, nodding towards Will Jackson. 'My friend here will see me off and take the horses away. Where is your ship?'

'She be tucked away very secret, in a creek towards Shoreham, Mr Barlow.'

'Good. And the crew?'

'Four men and a boy, sir, who will do my bidding without question. I am loaded with coal for Poole. When we stand well out to sea, towards the Isle of Wight, as will be natural with this wind, I'll change course and make direct for the coast of France.'

'When shall we sail?'

'Not until tomorrow, Mr Barlow. Being laid up in this creek I must wait for the tide to come in to float her, and for it to turn to take us out. It'll be betwixt seven and eight o'clock in the morning.'

'I had hoped to leave before that,' said Wilmot, 'what say you, Will?' He turned to his servant.

'We cannot alter the tides, sir; King Canute proved that long ago. It must be as the captain says.'

'You could go aboard and sleep in the little cabin,' said Captain Tattersall.

'That's what we will do,' said Wilmot. 'Landlord, fill our

glasses, we will drink with Captain Tattersall to the success of the voyage. And you, Will, on this occasion you may sit at the table and drink with us.'

'Thank you, sir,' said Will Jackson. As he sat down he favoured the embarrassed landlord with an exaggerated wink.

At about two o'clock in the morning the King, Lord Wilmot, and Captain Tattersall left the George by the back. The landlord took the King's hand without Tattersall seeing, and kissed it.

'A safe journey, Your Majesty,' he whispered, 'and a speedy return!'

'God bless you,' said the King, 'you have heartened me greatly, and, Master Smith, if I do come back, I shall not forget you.'

Colonel Gounter was waiting with the horses, and they rode a mile or so towards Shoreham. They dismounted when they came to the creek, scrambled over some rocks, and went down a short steep path to the *Surprise*. She was shored up with a timber, with only a few inches of water rippling about her keel. A short ladder was leaning against her hull and when the Captain went aboard the other three withdrew a little to talk privately.

'This is the moment I have long dreamed of,' said the King. 'A ship to take me to France.'

'I will wait with the horses here, Sire,' said Colonel Gounter, 'until you are safely at sea. If there should be any danger you can get away quickly.'

'Thank you, Gounter. These last few hours may prove to be the most trying of all. But this is a well chosen spot, and I shall pass the time in sleep.'

They stood together in companionable silence for a minute or two. The only sound was the lazy wash of the waves among the rocks at the mouth of the creek. The sea was calm, the air warm, and the sky was clear and full of stars. Then the King took Colonel Gounter's hand and said good-bye, and climbed the ladder to the deck of the *Surprise*.

In the little cabin he took off his boots, lay down on one of the bunks, and was soon asleep. Lord Wilmot sat on the other bunk or, when he became too sleepy, he went on deck. Gounter had tethered the horses and was sitting against a convenient rock, where he had a good view of the path leading to the creek. Captain Tattersall was asleep in his own cabin. Slowly the time passed, until the cold light of morning crept into the eastern sky.

When his guests went Mr Smith tidied their room, and very carefully locked the glass the King had used in a small cupboard. Then he shut up the inn and went to bed. About an hour later he was awakened by a violent knocking on the door. He put his head out of the curtains which hung round his bed and listened. He heard voices outside, and the rattle of hooves on the stones.

'What's that, William?' said his wife, sitting up in bed.

'People, my dear, at the door.'

'At this time of night! Well, go and see to them. Perhaps they are rich travellers.'

Mr Smith got out of bed, pulled on his boots, set his night-cap more firmly on his head, and went to the window.

'Who's there?' he said.

'Ah, there you are! I'm a captain of Militia. Come and let us in, and be quick!'

'Very good, Captain,' said Smith.

'Soldiers,' said his wife, 'at this time? What will they want?'

'How should I know!' said Smith, testy because he was very frightened.

He went downstairs, trying to think of what he would say and not succeeding, and unbarred the door. The officer walked in, followed by a sergeant and four troopers. A dozen or so others waited outside.

'What visitors have you had tonight?' said the captain.

'Let me think. Four soldiers off duty, Captain, a merchant

travelling to Lewes, and the Customs Officer. Oh, and two gentlemen going I know not whither and a sea captain.'

'The Colonel has been informed that a man who might be Charles Stuart was seen riding in company with another man in this direction this evening.'

'Charles Stuart, in these parts, Captain?'

'Apparently. He was described as being over two yards tall, and was dressed as a serving-man, in plain grey. He was riding a chestnut horse.'

'I've seen no chestnut horse, Captain.'

'I'm not looking for the horse, you fool! Have you seen this tall young man? What were the two gentlemen like who came here?'

'Well, Mr Barlow was about your height, Captain, a fine-built man like you, with fair hair. The other was a thin middle-aged man, a military gentleman I believe.'

'What's to-do, William?' Mrs Smith shouted from upstairs.

'A captain of Militia, my dear,' Smith called back, 'asking if the King is here.'

'The King, here!' she shouted. 'Is he drunk?'

'He is not the King,' said the captain, 'he is the rebel, Charles Stuart.'

'Your pardon, Captain. But King or rebel, whichever he is, he's not here!'

'Which way did the two gentlemen go?'

'I think they took the inland road, towards London, Captain.'

'Sergeant, search this inn from top to bottom,' said the captain briskly. 'I'll leave you four men and I'll take the rest up the Horsham road. Follow me when you've done.'

'Very good, sir,' said the sergeant.

The landlord watched the officer and some twenty troopers canter away and then he fetched one of his good bottles of sack. He opened it and put it in front of the sergeant.

'A glass of sack, Sergeant, to help you in your search,' he said.

'That's kind of you, landlord,' said the sergeant.

'Fancy Charles Stuart being in these parts!' said Smith.

'Aye, he's nearly netted now!' said the sergeant. 'He's had a good run, and he's plagued us proper. But his days are numbered. There's two regiments out searching, and every cross-road, every bridge, and every ford is guarded. D'you know where I think he's making for?'

'No, Sergeant, where?'

'Why, for London! He can lie low there better than anywhere. But we'll have him. Your health, landlord, and here's to the speedy end of our hunt!'

'I drink to that, Sergeant. Here's to the end of the hunt for the King.'

They clinked glasses and Smith saw in his mind's eye the little brig in the creek. He looked at the clock; it was four o'clock – three hours to high tide, three slow unhurried hours.

CHAPTER FOURTEEN

A FAIR WIND FOR FRANCE

IT was half past seven on the morning of 16th October, forty-two days after the battle of Worcester, when the *Surprise* moved slowly down the creek on the tide. Her sails were hoisted and tautened in the wind. Colonel Gounter heaved a sigh of relief as he saw the little brig gather way, and he looked over his shoulder for the hundredth time. The lonely stretch of shore was still deserted. The King would not be safe until the *Surprise* was out of reach of a faster boat, which might be sent after her by a suspicious official.

It was known in Shoreham that the *Surprise* was bound for Poole, and to avoid arousing any dangerous curiosity Captain Tattersall was sailing on the course he would have taken, coasting in a south-westerly direction towards the Isle of Wight. Such a course, with the light wind which was blowing, would keep the brig in sight of land for a long time. Not until she changed course southwards would Colonel Gounter's duty be done, so he sat down patiently to keep his vigil. Alone on the empty sea the brig seemed very conspicuous, and Gounter wondered how many soldiers, pausing in their zealous hunt for Charles Stuart, would turn to watch the ship.

It was not until five o'clock in the afternoon that the *Surprise* changed course to southward, and melted from sight. Colonel Gounter stood up and stretched. He felt suddenly lonely; the King was safe, but he had lost a friend.

The King and Lord Wilmot spent most of the day on the after-part of the deck. Occasionally they glanced behind them, but for most of the time they looked towards the horizon. They ate simple ships' fare of biscuit and drank small ale, and fell into the tranquil mood of a sea voyage.

When Captain Tattersall changed course and headed straight out to sea he called the oldest of his men to him.

'Jenkins, I have changed course because we are running across to France, to put this gentleman and his servant ashore.'

'So that's the game, Cap'n,' said Jenkins, pulling at his pipe and looking at Lord Wilmot.

'You will be given two sovereigns for your pains, the other men a sovereign each and the boy, Jack, ten shillings. If it were known that we'd been to France without permission we might all find ourselves in gaol. So keep your mouth shut. You understand?'

'I'll see they say nothing about it, Cap'n,' he said. He looked at the King again, and puffed a cloud of tobacco smoke in his face.

'Stand farther off, man,' said Tattersall, 'and don't stare at the passengers!'

'All right,' grumbled the seaman, 'a cat may look at a king, mayn't it?' and he went forward to the others.

Lord Wilmot looked startled, but the King laughed lightly. 'He is something of a philosopher, that worthy seaman!' he said.

'Yes, Harry Jenkins always has an answer,' said Tattersall. He too looked at the King, and with a new interest.

'Will,' said Lord Wilmot, 'it is time for us to sup, come to the cabin.'

They could not tell whether or not Captain Tattersall had guessed their secret. But if he had he kept it to himself and showed no change in his attitude.

That night the King slept in the cabin, but he was out on deck with Lord Wilmot as dawn broke. The wind was stronger and the brig surged forward, from time to time tossing spray over her bows. As the light increased they saw a dark line on the horizon – the coast of France.

'Do you see it, Henry?' he said.

'Yes, Your Majesty. At last!'

'I know. Even now I dare hardly hope. We shall be safe, and yet, for all the perils and discomfort, there is a part of me which looks back wistfully. For I gain safety only by leaving my own country.'

'Leaving it but to return, Sire, when your people come to their senses.'

'I wonder, Henry! And yet, I think you are right. On one thing I am resolved. I shall not try again to win my crown by force of arms. I shall only return when they want me, and send for me.'

By mid-morning the *Surprise* was less than two miles from the shore, which Tattersall recognized as the little port of Fécamp. The tide was running against them and the wind had backed, so that they could not get any nearer. The cock-boat was unshipped and the King and Wilmot said good-bye to Captain Tattersall.

'You have done us a great service, Captain,' said Wilmot, 'which we shall not forget.'

'Perhaps I shall see you again, sir,' said Tattersall. He spoke to Wilmot, but he looked at the King, 'when you come back.'

'Rest assured, Captain,' said the King, 'that one day, God willing, I shall seek you out to thank you again.'

'I should be most honoured,' said Tattersall, 'and when that occurs I might change the name of my ship.'

'Change the name of your ship?' said the King.

'Yes, sir, I thought perhaps, *The Royal Escape*.'

'An excellent name, Captain,' said the King, 'and she might be listed in the Royal Navy, and you commissioned Captain. Yes, that would be most appropriate. And now, thank you and – good-bye.'

'Good-bye – sir,' said Captain Tattersall.

They climbed over the side and dropped into the little boat. Seaman Jenkins pushed her off and started to pull steadily for the shore. Captain Tattersall watched them from the deck of the *Surprise*, his face showing nothing of his thoughts.

Some hours later two horsemen rode into the galleried court-yard of the best hotel in Rouen, L'Étoile. They dismounted and an ostler ran out to take their horses, and then looked at them with misgiving.

The landlord came out, his face set in a ready smile of welcome. But the smile vanished when he saw the two visitors.

'Ah, landlord,' said the King in fluent French, 'we want the best room you have. And we are hungry, so we will eat immediately, the best you have and the rarest wine. We also want hot water and towels, and send us a good barber.'

'Indeed,' said the landlord, sarcastically, 'the best room, the best food, hot water, rare wine, a barber! Oh yes! We do not receive vagabonds such as you at L'Étoile. So begone, the pair of you!'

'Vagabonds!' said the King, 'how dare you! Listen, you stupid man, I am the King of England!'

'And I am the Emperor of Russia!' said the landlord. 'No, begone for I am busy.'

The King suddenly began to laugh. Wilmot had not under-stood all the conversation, but the purport was obvious from the landlord's expression and gestures.

'Oh, Henry,' said the King, 'this is ridiculous! After all we have been through; hunted high and low, pursued, disguised, travelling at night, hiding in an oak-tree, skulking in secret rooms, and now we are safe and free, and we are taken for a pair of vagabonds! It's quite natural! Look at us! We have dirty faces and hands, our clothes are stained and creased, we are unshaven, and our hair matted! The question is, how can we convince him!'

Two gentlemen had come down the stairs from the gallery which ran round the courtyard, and they looked with surprise at the shabby and unkempt men standing in front of the indignant landlord.

'Who on earth can these fellows be, James?' one said in English.

Lord Wilmot looked up. 'Sire,' he said, 'they are English!'

'Thank goodness!' said the King. 'Go and explain our predicament to them.'

The two Englishmen looked uneasy as Lord Wilmot went over to them.

'Your pardon, gentlemen,' said Wilmot, 'but I believe you are English.'

'We are,' said one of them.

'Then I beg of you do me a service. We are in some difficulty with the landlord.'

'A service? What service?' the Englishman said contemptuously.

'Come and be presented to my companion, then you will understand.'

'Really, you must excuse us. We have an appointment.'

'That must wait,' said Lord Wilmot firmly. 'First allow me to introduce myself. I am Henry, Lord Wilmot. And you are ...?'

'Lord Wilmot!' The Englishmen spoke the title doubtfully, looking meaningly at Wilmot's stained clothes.

'Please, your names, gentlemen,' Wilmot said.

'I am James Sambourne, a merchant of London. My friend, also a merchant, is Mr Parker.'

'Good. Then come with me, please.' Wilmot led them to the King, who had watched the conversation with amusement. Wilmot bowed.

'Your Majesty,' he said, 'I beg leave to present Mr Sambourne and Mr Parker, merchants of London.'

'I am exceedingly pleased to meet you, my friends,' said the King.

The two Englishmen had opened their eyes wide when Wilmot said 'Your Majesty'. They looked at each other, then at Wilmot and then, timidly, at the King.

'You are ... are you ... the King?' said Sambourne.

'I am,' said Charles, 'newly arrived from England after being hunted for six weeks, which accounts for my somewhat unusual appearance!'

'But it's true!' said Parker suddenly, 'it really *is* His Majesty! I can see it now! Heavens above!'

He dropped on one knee and Sambourne did the same.

'Your Majesty,' said Parker, 'I beg of you to forgive our ignorance and stupidity. You see – we could not believe – I mean – we never thought ...'

'Come, my friends, all is forgiven! I confess I am not looking my best. I beg of you to convince mine host here that I am indeed the King of England!'

There was no need. The landlord had watched it all with increasing astonishment, which had quickly changed to dismay when he realized that the visitor he had insulted was indeed the King of England. He was a fat man, and he trembled in every limb as he went forward and begged forgiveness.

'Come, I do not hold it against you,' said the King, 'but you must make amends with good service.'

'Everything I have, Your Majesty, is yours to command,' said the landlord. He clapped his hands and shouted, 'Maria, Émile, Jules, Anne-Marie, Henri, Ercole, come quick, come I say.' He turned to the King. 'Your Majesty shall want for nothing, nothing at all, while you honour L'Étoile with your presence.'

The hostelry buzzed with activity. Baths of hot water, freshly scented, were provided. Food was prepared with the greatest care; bottles of wine were brought from darkest corners of the cellars. A barber was hurriedly fetched. Within half an hour Mr Sambourne set off for Paris, carrying a letter to the King of France and another to the King's mother. The best coach in Rouen was cleaned and polished and the axles were greased. Horses were groomed and harness was polished. The mayor of Rouen hurried round to L'Étoile with the principal citizens, and a large crowd gathered outside.

Bathed and groomed, and wearing the best clothes which Mr Parker possessed, the King sat down to the splendid meal the landlord set before him. Lord Wilmot filled the King's glass with wine.

'Well, Henry, it is over,' the King said as he tasted the wine. 'They hunted me for forty-two days, and by the grace of God and the devotion of many friends I have been preserved. I hope one day I can reward those friends. You have been my most constant companion, Henry, and I have decided to create you Earl of Rochester. Yes, it is over! In a few days I shall go to Paris, openly, as King of England. They tried hard, did Cromwell's men.' He sipped his wine. 'Yes, it is finished, the Hunt Royal!'

EPILOGUE

KING CHARLES spent nine years in exile. In 1658 Oliver Cromwell died, and his son, Richard, became Lord Protector of England, but the next year he resigned. A quarrel developed between Parliament and the Army as to which should govern, and the people of England became tired of the quarrels for power. They wanted to return to the old ways of the monarchy. Thus it fell out that the King was asked to come back.

On 26th May 1660 King Charles II landed at Dover, and three days later he entered London. Church bells pealed joyously, cannons fired their solemn salutes, and the crowds cheered their welcome. The King had come into his own again.

The people who had helped him to escape were remembered and rewarded. It became the custom for everyone to wear an oak-apple on 29th May, 'Oak-apple Day', in memory of the Boscobel oak, and as a reminder of the King's return to London after his exile. Charles II reigned for twenty-five years. He was a shrewd king; and as a man he was clever, witty, and so gay that he was given the nickname of The Merry Monarch.